W9-BNY-343

March of America Facsimile Series

Number 98

Campaigning with Crook
and Stories of Army Life.

Charles King

Campaigning with Crook and Stories of Army Life

by Charles King

ANN ARBOR
UNIVERSITY MICROFILMS, INC.
A Subsidiary of Xerox Corporation

WINGATE COLLEGE LIBRARY.
WINGATE, N. C.

XEROX

COPYRIGHT © BY UNIVERSITY MICROFILMS, INC., 1966

ALL RIGHTS RESERVED

LIBRARY OF CONGRESS CATALOG CARD NO. 66-26366

MANUFACTURED IN THE UNITED STATES OF AMERICA

Foreword

The story of the gradual annihilation of Indian life
on the western plains is grim and sordid but not to
such a writer as Charles King, a soldier and novelist,
who participated in the Indian wars and contrived
to make his experiences sound like his own sentimental fiction that gave him something of a reputa-
tion as a writer in his time. His *Campaigning with
Crook and Stories of Army Life*, first published as
sketches in the Milwaukee *Sentinel* and gathered into
a volume and published in Milwaukee in 1880, com-
bines both the factual and the fictional in one book
that well illustrates King's literary skill. The volume
had a later printing in New York in 1890.

King wrote innumerable stories of army life. In his
Who's Who in America biography, King boasted that
he had fought in every United States war between
1861 and 1920. When he wrote *Campaigning with
Crook*, he was a captain in the United States Army.
He ultimately retired as a major general and served
as chief of staff in 1930.

King conveniently begins *Campaigning with Crook*
a few days after General George A. Crook's defeat at
the hands of Crazy Horse with a combination of Sioux
and Cheyenne warriors at the battle of Rosebud

Creek, Montana, on June 17, 1876. That saves King the embarrassment of explaining his commanding officer's discomfiture at the hands of savages whom the writer treats with faint contempt. On June 25, Crazy Horse and Sitting Bull wiped out General George A. Custer's command at the battle of the Little Bighorn, Montana. King talks about the massacre and describes the pursuit of the Indians as they withdrew toward the north. The tone of the campaign, as described by King, is that of a summer's lark.

The Sioux War of 1876 was the inevitable result of the discovery of gold in the Black Hills and the migration into that territory of swarms of miners. The United States government had guaranteed to the Indians this land for as long as grass grows and the waters run, but the discovery of gold altered matters. Somehow the Sioux had to be eliminated and miners allowed to exploit the gold in the hills. The Indians did not take kindly to the invasion of their territory by whites; they would not permit free passage across their lands by emigrants; and they would not stay on reservations set aside for them. The Sioux War of 1876 resulted, and General George A. Crook, commander of the Department of the Platte, spent a year in the field with his army trying to discipline the Indians. In the end, Crazy Horse surrendered and Sitting Bull took refuge in Canada.

General Crook was somewhat more enlightened and more understanding of the Indian problem than some of his superiors, notably General Sheridan and General Sherman, who thought that extermination would be the quickest, safest, and best solution of the Indian problem.

King's *Campaigning with Crook* is a good example of the type of writing that romanticized the Indian wars. Such works spawned countless dime novels and, later, innumerable B-grade motion pictures that still infest television screens.

King was much impressed with "Buffalo Bill" Cody, who left his theatrical show in the East to serve for a time with the Fifth Cavalry, to which King was attached. Cody heard the news of Crook's war with the Sioux while playing at Wilmington, Delaware, King reports, and "rushed through the performance, paid off his company, took the midnight express, and four days later sprang from the Union Pacific at Cheyenne, and was speedily exchanging greetings with an eager group of his old comrades, reinstated as chief scout of the regiment." King goes on to eulogize Cody. "One of his best plays is founded on the incidents of our fight of the 17th of July with the Cheyenne Indians on the War Bonnet, for it was there he killed the warrior Yellow Hand in as plucky a single combat on both sides as is ever witnessed." This is a fair example of King's narration. Sketches of General Crook and Crazy Horse in the *Dictionary of American Biography* will give essential information about the campaign which King romanticized. See also *General George Crook: His Autobiography*, edited by Martin F. Schmitt (Norman, Oklahoma, 1946-47) and Robert G. Athearn, *William Tecumseh Sherman, and the Settlement of the West* (Norman, Oklahoma, 1956).

CAMPAIGNING WITH CROOK
AND STORIES OF ARMY LIFE

BY

CAPTAIN CHARLES KING, U.S.A.

AUTHOR OF "BETWEEN THE LINES" "A WAR-TIME WOOING"
ETC., ETC.

ILLUSTRATED

NEW YORK

HARPER & BROTHERS, FRANKLIN SQUARE

1890

Entered according to Act of Congress, in the year 1880, by

CHARLES KING,

In the Office of the Librarian of Congress, at Washington.

———

Copyright, 1890, by HARPER & BROTHERS.

———

All rights reserved.

PREFACE.

TEN years ago, at the request of the editor of a paper at my old home, these sketches of the Sioux Campaign of 1876 were written and, finding favor with comrades to whom a few were sent, were published in pamphlet form. Now, reinforced by certain other sketches which have since appeared, they are given a new framework.

They were the first-fruits, so to speak, of a pen that has since been seldom idle. They were rough sketches, to be sure, but no rougher than the campaign; and in the early days of a divorce from associations that were very dear, and of a return to surroundings once familiar, yet, after twenty years of absence, so changed that a cat in a strange garret could hardly have felt less at home, I laid their faint tribute of respect and honor at the feet of the soldier who had been our commander in the wild days in Arizona, our leader from the Platte to the Yellowstone and our comrade in every hardship and privation—Brigadier-General George Crook, United States Army.

Only enough of these pamphlets were printed to reach the few hundred comrades who rode the grim circuit of "The Bad Lands" in that eventful centennial year. The little edition was long ago exhausted. The years that followed only served to strengthen the ties that bound me to the revered commander of old cavalry days. Many a name recorded in these pages no longer graces our muster-rolls. Mason, our soldier major, gallant Emmet Crawford, brave old Munson, daring Philo Clark; Rodgers and Price, Egan and Dewees, Bache and Hunter, have been called from the ranks in which they won such honor, and, only a few short months ago, the leader whom they so faithfully served rejoined them on the farther shore of the dark and silent river. The mountains and prairies over which we marched and fought know no longer the war-cry of painted savage or the din of thrilling combat. Herds of browsing cattle crowd the lovely valleys through which we drove the buffalo. Peaceful homes and smiling villages dot the broad Northwest where hardly a roof-tree was in place when Crook essayed the task of subjugating the foeman to settlement and civilization. Another star had been added to the one awarded him for the campaign which left the fierce Apaches conquered and disarmed. The highest grade in the army had been attained when, all too soon, he was summoned to answer to his name, " beyond the veil."

Better pens than mine shall tell our people of his long years of brave and faithful service in which this campaign of '76—so pregnant with interest to us who rode the trail, and with result to a waiting nation—was, after all, only an episode ; but, just as in honor and in loyalty, these faint pictures of the stirring scenes through which he led us were inscribed to him at their birth, so now, with added honor and in affectionate remembrance tenfold increased, is that humble tribute renewed.

CHARLES KING,
Captain, U. S. A.

CONTENTS.

ILLUSTRATIONS.

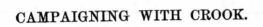

CAMPAIGNING WITH CROOK.

CHAPTER I.

THE disastrous battle on the Little Horn, which resulted in the annihilation of General Custer and his five favorite companies of the Seventh Cavalry, occurred on the 25th of June, 1876. On the 4th of that month, we of the Fifth Cavalry were far to the south, scattered over the boundless prairies of Kansas. Regimental headquarters and four companies occupied the cosey quarters of Fort Hays, nearly midway between Leavenworth and Denver, Missouri and the mountains, and Company " K," of which I then was first lieutenant, had pitched its tents along the banks of a winding fork of the Smoky Hill River, wondering why we had been "routed out" from our snug barracks and stables at Fort Riley, and ordered to proceed, "equipped for field service," to Hays City, by rail. Ordinarily, Uncle Sam pays the costly railway fare for horsemen and their steeds only when danger is imminent. The two posts were but a week's easy march apart; not a hostile Indian had been seen or heard of in all Kansas since the previous winter; General Pope, who commanded the department, had won the hearts of the ladies and children of the officers' families by predicting that there would be no

separation from husbands and fathers that summer
at least; all the ladies had "joined," and, after our
long sojourn in the wilds of Arizona, where but few
among them had been able to follow us, we were re-
joicing in their presence and luxuriating in the pretty
homes ornamented and blessed by their dainty handi-
work. Some among their number had never before
appeared in garrison, and were taking their first lesson in frontier experience. Some, too, had only been
with us six short weeks, and did not dream that the
daily parades in which they took so much delight,
the sweet music of our band, the brilliant uniforms
and dancing plumes that lent such color and life to
rapid drill or stately guard-mounting, were one and
all but part and parcel of the preparation for scenes
more stirring, far less welcome to such gentle eyes.

Fort Hays was joyous with mirth and music and
merry laughter, for some of the ladies of the regiment had brought with them from the distant East
younger sisters or friends, to whom army life on the
plains was a revelation, and in whose honor a large
barrack-room had been transformed into "the loveli-
est place in the world for a german," and Strauss's
sweetest music rose and fell in witching invitation
after the evening tattoo. Riding, driving, and hunting parties were of daily occurrence, and more than
one young fellow's heart seemed in desperate jeopardy
when the summons came.

The sun was setting in a cloudless sky as I reined
in my horse in front of General Carr's quarters and
dismounted, to make my report of a three days' hunt

along the valley of the Saline for stampeded horses.
The band, in their neat summer dress, were grouped
around the flagstaff, while the strains of "Soldaten
Lieder" thrilled through the soft evening air, and,
fairly carried away by the cadence of the sweet music, a party of young ladies and officers had dropped
their croquet mallets and were waltzing upon the
green carpet of the parade. Seated upon the veran-
das other ladies and older officers were smilingly
watching the pretty scene, and on the western side
of the quadrangle the men in their white stable frocks
were just breaking ranks after marching up from the
never-neglected care of their horses. Half a dozen
laughing children were chasing one another in noisy
glee, their bright sashes and dainty dresses gleaming
in the last rays of the golden orb. The general himself was gazing thoughtfully at the distant line of
willows that fringed the banks of the stream, and
holding an open newspaper in his hand as I entered
and made my report.

"Have you heard the news?" he asked me. "Schuyler has gone to join General Crook as aide-de-camp.
Got a telegram from him just after you left on this
scout, and started last night. It's my belief that
Crook will have a big campaign, and that we'll be
sent for."

Ten minutes after, as the trumpets rang out the
"retreat," and the last echoes of the evening gun
died away over the rolling prairie, we noted a horseman coming at rapid gait along the dusty road from
Hays City, as the railway station was hopefully

named. He disappeared among the foliage in the
creek bottom. The soft hush of twilight fell upon
the garrison, the band had gone away to supper, the
bevy of sweet-faced girls with their tireless escorts
had gathered with a number of officers and ladies in
front of the general's quarters, where he and I were
still in conversation, when the horseman, a messenger
from the telegraph office, reappeared in our midst.
"Despatch for you, general; thought you'd better
have it at once," was all he said, as he handed it to
"the chief," and, remounting, cantered away.

Carr opened the ugly brown envelope and took
out, not one, but three sheets of despatch paper, closely written, and began to read. Looking around upon
the assembled party, I noticed that conversation had
ceased and a dozen pair of eyes were eagerly scrutinizing the face of the commanding officer. Anxious
hearts were beating among those young wives and
mothers, and the sweet girl-faces had paled a little in
sympathy with the dread that shone all too plainly in
the eyes of those who but so recently had undergone
long and painful separation from soldier husbands.
The general is a sphinx; he gives no sign. Slowly
and carefully he reads the three pages; then goes
back and begins over again. At last, slowly, thoughtfully he folds it, replaces the fateful despatch in its
envelope, and looks up expectant of question. His
officers, restrained by discipline, endeavor to appear
unconcerned, and say nothing. The ladies, either from
dread of the tidings or awe of him, *look* volumes, but
are silent. Human nature asserts itself, however, and

the man and the commander turns to me with, "Well, what did I tell you?" And so we got our orders for the Sioux campaign of 1876.

To the officers, of course, it was an old story. There was not one of our number who had not seen hard campaigning and sharp Indian fighting before. But could we have had our choice, we would have preferred some less abrupt announcement. Hardly a word was spoken as the group broke up and the ladies sought their respective homes, but the bowed heads and hidden faces of many betrayed the force of the blow.

The officers remained with General Carr to receive his instructions. There was no time to lose, and the note of preparation sounded on the spot. General Sheridan's orders directed four companies from Fort Hays to proceed at once to Cheyenne by rail, and there await the coming of the more distant companies —eight in all, to go on this, the first alarm.

Companies "A," "B," "D," and "K" were designated to go; "E" to stay and "take care of the shop." Those to go were commanded by married officers, each of whom had to leave wife and family in garrison. "E" had a bachelor captain, and a lieutenant whose better half was away in the East, so the ladies of the regiment were ready to mob the general for his selection; but there was wisdom in it. In ten minutes the news was all over the post. A wild Celtic "Hurray, fellows, we're going for to join Crook," was heard in the barracks, answered by shouts of approval and delight from every Paddy in the command. Ours is a mixed array of nationalities—Mulligan and Meiswinkel, Crapaud and John Bull, stand shoulder to shoulder with Yanks from every portion of the country. In four regiments only is exclusiveness as to race permitted by law. Only darkies can join their ranks. Otherwise, there is a promiscuous arrangement which, oddly enough, has many a recommendation. They balance one another as it were—the phlegmatic Teuton and the fiery Celt, mercurial Gaul and stolid Anglo-Saxon. Dashed and strongly tinctured with the clear-headed individuality of the American, they make up a company which for *personnel* is admirably adapted to the wants of our democratic service. The company of the Fifth Cavalry most strongly flavored with Irish element in the ranks was commanded by Captain Emil Adam, an old German soldier, whose broken English on drill was the delight of his men. "The representative Paddy," as he calls himself, Captain Nick Nolan, of the Tenth Cavalry, has an Ethiopian lieutenant (a West-Pointer) and sixty of the very best darkies that ever stole chickens. But wherever you meet them, the first to hurray at the chance of a fight is the Pat, and no matter how gloomy or dismal the campaign, if there be any fun to be extracted from its incidents, he is the man to find it.

And so our Irishmen gave vent to their joy, and with whistling and singing the men stowed away their helmets and full - dress uniforms, their handsome belts and equipments, and lovingly reproduced the old Arizona slouch hats and "thimble belts," and the next evening our Fort Hays command, in two special trains, was speeding westward as fast as the Kansas Pacific could carry us.   The snow-capped peaks of the Rockies hove in sight next day, and Denver turned out in full force to see us go through. At evening on the 7th, we were camping on the broad prairie near Cheyenne.   Here Major Upham joined us with Company "I."   A week after we were off for Laramie.   On the 22d, our companies were ordered straight to the north to find the crossing of the broad Indian trail from the Red Cloud and Spotted Tail reservations, by which hundreds of Indians were known to be going to the support of Sitting Bull and Crazy Horse.

We were to hide in the valley of the South Cheyenne, near the base of the Black Hills, and cut off the Indian supplies.   Buffalo Bill had joined us, his old comrades of the Sioux war of 1868–69 ; and though we feared the Indians would be quick to detect our presence, and select others of a dozen routes to the Powder River country, we hoped to be able to nab a few.

On the 24th, we had begun our march at 6 A.M. from the Cardinal's Chair, at the head of the Niobrara, and before noon had descended into the valley of "Old Woman's Fork," of the South Cheyenne.   We had with us two half-breed Sioux scouts and an Indian boy, "Little Bat," who had long been employed by the Fort Laramie officers as a reliable guide.   Camping at noon along the stream, I was approached by Major Stanton, who had joined our column under instructions from General Sheridan, and informed that he was going to push ahead of the column at once, as the scouts reported recent Indian signs. It was necessary, he said, that he should get to the Cheyenne as quickly as possible, and he wanted me to go as commander of the escort. In half an hour we were in saddle again, Major Stanton with his blunderbuss of a rifle, "Little Bat" in his semi-civilized garb, Lieutenant Keyes with forty men of Company "C," and myself. The general detained me a moment to convey some earnest instructions, and to post me on certain points in Sioux warfare which experience with Apaches was supposed to have dulled, and, with the promise, "I'll follow on your trail to-morrow," waved his hand, and in two minutes we were out of sight down the winding valley.

Three P.M. is early on a long June day. We rode swiftly, steadily, but cautiously northward; the valley widened out to east and west; we made numerous cut-offs among the bends of the stream, crossing low ridges, at each one of which Bat, well to the front, would creep to the top, keenly scrutinize all the country around, and signal "come on." At 5 o'clock he suddenly halted and threw himself from his horse, and I cantered forward to see what was up. We had struck our first trail of the campaign, and the yielding soil was thick with pony tracks. Coming from the east, the direction of the reservation, they led straight down the valley, and we followed. Every now and then other tracks from the east joined those we were on, and though at least four or five days old, they were of interest. Half an hour before sunset, far off among the hills to the northeast, a thin column of smoke shot up into the clear sky. Ten minutes more another rose in the west. They were Sioux signals, and we were discovered.   But the country was open all around us ; not a tree except the cottonwoods along the narrow stream-bed, no fear of ambuscade, and we must not halt until within sight of the Cheyenne valley ; so on we go.   Just at twilight, Bat, five hundred yards in front, circles his horse rapidly to the left, and again I join him.   It is the recent trail of a war - party of Sioux, crossing the valley, and disappearing among the low hills to the northwest.   They number fifty warriors, and those whose tracks we have been following took the same direction — the short cut towards the Big Horn mountains.   Our march is very cautious now—advance, flankers, and rear guard of old, tried soldiers, well out ; but on we jog through the gathering darkness, and at nine P.M., as we ride over a ridge, Bat points out to me a long, low line of deeper shade, winding six or seven miles away in the moonlight.   It is the timber along the Cheyenne, and now we may hunt for water and give our tired horses rest and grass.   The valley is broad ; the water lies only in scanty pools among the rocks in the stream-bed.   There has been no rain for a month, and there is not a blade of grass nearer than the bluffs, a mile away.   Our horses drink eagerly, and then in silence we fill our canteens and move off towards the hills.   Here I find a basin about two hundred yards in diameter, in which we "half lariat" and hobble our horses ; dig holes in the ground, wherein, with sage brush for fuel, we build little fires and boil our coffee, while Keyes and I take a dozen of our men and post them around our bivouac at points commanding every approach.   No Indian can reach us unseen through that moonlight.   No Indian cares to attack at night, unless he has a "sure thing ;" and though from five different points we catch the blaze of signal fires, we defy surprise, and with ready carbine by our side we eat our crisp bacon, sip the welcome tin of steaming coffee, then light our pipes and chat softly in the cool night air.   Little we dream that two hundred miles away Custer is making his night ride to death.   Our supports are only twenty-five miles away.   We dread no attack in such force that we cannot "stand off" until Carr can reach us, and, as I make my rounds among the sentinels to see that all are vigilant, the words of the Light Cavalryman's song are sounding in my ears :

> "The ring of a bridle, the stamp of a hoof,
>   Stars above and the wind in the tree ;
> A bush for a billet, a rock for a roof,
>   Outpost duty's the duty for me.
> Listen ! A stir in the valley below—
>   The valley below is with riflemen crammed,
> Cov'ring the column and watching the foe ;
>   Trumpet-Major ! Sound and be d——."

Bang !   There's a shot from below, and the bivouac springs to life.

CHAPTER II.

THE TRAIL AND THE CHASE.

A SHOT in the dead of night from an outpost in the heart of the Indian country is something that soon ceases to be either exciting or of great interest, but the first that is heard on the campaign makes the pulses bound. Men sprang to their feet, horses pawed and snorted, and the sergeant of the guard and myself made rapid time to the point from which the alarm had come. There was the sentinel alone, unharmed, but perturbed in spirit. To the question, somewhat sternly put, "Who fired that shot?" he replies, with evident chagrin, "I did, sir; somethin' was crawlin' right up that holler, an' I challenged an' he didn't answer, an' I fired; but danged if I know what it was." Before there is time to say a word of rebuke, plainly enough in the bright moonlight something *does* come crawling up out of a "hollow" two hundred yards away—something of a yellow or reddish brown, on four legs, with a long, smooth, sneaking shamble that carries the quadruped rapidly over the ground, then changes to an ungainly lope, which takes him to a safe distance in six seconds; and there the creature turns, squats on his haunches, and coolly surveys us. Turning away in silent indignation, as I

WINGATE COLLEGE LIBRARY
WINGATE N. C.

get almost out of earshot it is some comfort to hear
the sergeant's pithy commentary, " Ye wall-eyed gut-
ter-snipe, your grandmother would ha' known that was
nothin' but a cayote."

Then follows the inevitable volley of chaff with
which the Paddy greets every blunder on the part of
his fellow-soldiers, and for a few minutes the silent
bivouac is rollicking with fun.   That some recent attempt has been made to instruct the troopers of Company " C " in the *finesse* of sentry duty is apparent
from the shouted query, " Hi, Sullivan, if it was *two*
cayotes would you advance the saynior or the junior
wid the countersign ?" at which there is a roar, and
Lieutenant Keyes visibly blushes.   In half an hour
all is quiet again.   Officers and men, we watch turn
and turn about during the night, undisturbed, save at
3 o'clock the outlying sentries report that they distinctly heard the rapid beat of many hoofs dying
away towards the west.

We are astir at the first gray of dawn, rolling our
blankets and promptly saddling, for we must ride
well down the Cheyenne and find the Mini Pusa, the
dry north fork, before breakfast can be attended to.
No stirring trumpet marks our reveille.   We mount
in silence, and like shadowy spectres ride away northward in the broadening valley.   The stars are not yet
paling in the west, but Bat's quick eye detects fresh
hoof-prints not two hours old in the springy soil of the
hillside, half a mile out from camp.   Sure enough.
They had prowled around us during the night, longing for our scalps, but not daring to attack.   Only a

few venturesome spies had galloped down to take observations, and had then ridden away to join their brothers in arms, and plot our destruction. We laughed as we shook our bridle - reins and jogged along, thinking how confounded they would be when they caught sight of our main body, who, with General Carr at their head, would be along by noon. A six - mile ride brought us into the belt of cottonwoods and willows along the bed of the stream, but the South Cheyenne had sunk out of sight. Broad reaches of streaked and rippled sand wound through the timber, clearly showing where, earlier in the season, a rapid, sweeping torrent had borne great logs and heaps of brushwood upon its tawny breast; but it had dwindled away to nothing, and our thirsty horses looked reproachfully at their masters as, dismounting, we ploughed up the yielding sand, in hopes of finding the needed water beneath. This is one of the dismal peculiarities of the streams of the Far West. On the 1st of May we would have found that valley barely fordable; on the 25th of June it was as dry as a bone.

Mounting again, and scattering through the timber "down stream," a shout from Major Stanton had the effect of the trumpet rally on skirmish drill.

Our party came together with eager haste, and found him under a steep bank, shaded by willows, his horse fetlock deep in what remained of a once deep pool; and two or three at a time our chargers slaked their thirst. It was poor water—warm, soapy, alkaline—but better than none at all.

Just before noon we were clambering up the hills on the northeast of the Mini Pusa. Our orders were to proceed with the utmost caution on nearing the trail. General Sheridan had clearly indicated that it must cross the valley of the South Cheyenne some distance west of the Beaver, and very near its confluence with the Mini Pusa. Stanton and I, with our field-glasses in hand, were toiling up through the yielding, sandy soil with Little Bat; Lieutenant Keyes and the escort, leading their horses, following. Once at the top of the ridge we felt sure of seeing the country to the eastward, and hardly had Bat reached the crest and peered cautiously over than he made a quick gesture which called the major and myself to his side. He pointed to the southeast, and, sweeping our glasses in that direction, we plainly saw the broad, beaten track. It looked like a great highway, deserted and silent, and it led from the thick timber in the Cheyenne valley straight to the southeast up the distant slope, and disappeared over the dim, misty range of hills in the direction of the Red Cloud and Spotted Tail reservations.

General Sheridan was right. Sitting in his distant office in Chicago, he was so thoroughly informed that he could order out his cavalry to search through a region hitherto known only to the Sioux, and tell them just where they would find the highway by which the vast hordes of hostiles under Sitting Bull were receiving daily reinforcements and welcome supplies of ammunition from the agencies three and four hundred miles to the southeast.

This was the traffic which General Carr and the Fifth Cavalry were ordered to break up ; and here, just at noon, our little band of three officers and forty men, far in the advance, had struck the trail, as General Sheridan predicted. Keeping horses and men well under cover, we crept to a farther ridge, and from there our glasses commanded a grand sweep of country : the valley of the South Cheyenne for fifty miles to the southeastward, until the stream itself was lost in the tortuous cañon of the Southern Black Hills ; the great, towering range of the Black Hills themselves forty miles to the eastward, and the lone peak far to the northeast that the Sioux called (phonetically spelling) Heengha Kahga. The earliest maps simplified that into "Inyan Kara," and now the school-children of Deadwood talk glibly of the big hill that, higher than Harney's or Custer's Peak, their geography terms the "Indian Carry." Why can't we keep the original names ?"

Once thoroughly satisfied of our proximity to the trail, Major Stanton directed the escort to retrace its steps to the thick timber along the Mini Pusa, where it would be out of sight, while he and I, with our powerful binoculars, kept watch upon the Indian highway. The afternoon was hot and cloudless ; not a breath of air stirred the clumps of sage-bush, the only vegetation along the bluffs and slopes. The atmosphere was dazzlingly clear, and objects were visible to us through our glasses that we knew to be miles away. The signal smokes to the west, and our front of the day before, had disappeared ; not a living thing

2

was in sight. Our men and horses were hidden among the dense cottonwoods a mile behind us, but, though invisible to us, we well knew that trusty eyes were keeping watch for the first signal from the hillside.

Three—four o'clock came, and not a soul had appeared upon the Indian trail. Away over the intervening ridge to the rear we could see the valley of Old Woman's Fork, down which we had come the day previous, and our glasses detected, by an hour after noon, clouds of dust rising high in air, harbingers of the march of General Carr and the main body. At last the major closed his glasses with a disgusted snap and the remark, "I don't believe there's an Indian stirring to-day."

Not in our sight—not within our hearing, perhaps. The blessed Sabbath stillness falls on all within our ken; our steeds are blinking, our men are drowsing in the leafy shades below. Only the rising dust, miles to the southward, reveals the coming of comrade soldiery. Far to the northwest, a single dark speck, floating against the blue of heaven, attracts the lingering inspection of my field-glass. Eagle or buzzard, I do not know. The slow, circling, stately flight in ascending spiral carries him beyond our vision, but from his altitude the snow-capped peaks of the Big Horn range are clearly visible, and on this still Sabbath afternoon those mighty peaks are looking down upon a scene of carnage, strife, and slaughter that, a week hence, told only by curt official despatches, will thrill a continent with horror. Even as we watch there on the slopes by the Mini Pusa, Stanton and I, grumbling at our want of luck in not sighting an Indian, many a true and trusted comrade, many an old cadet friend of boyish days, many a stalwart soldier is biting the dust along the Little Horn, and the names of Custer and his men are dropping from the muster-rolls. The heroes of a still mightier struggle, the victors of an immortal defence of national honor, are falling fast till all are gone, victims of a thankless warfare.

No wonder the Indians have no time to bother with us. We bivouac in undisturbed serenity that night, and join our regiment in the Cheyenne valley at noon next day without so much as an adventure. That night Company " I " is thrown forward to scout the trail, while the regiment camps out of sight among the cottonwoods, and for the next week we keenly watch the neighborhood, all the companies making thorough scouts in each direction, but finding nothing of consequence. Small parties of Indians are chased, but easily escape, and there isn't a doubt that the reservation Indians know of our whereabouts, and so avoid us.

Late in the afternoon of July 1st, our new colonel, Wesley Merritt, famous as a cavalry commander during the War of the Rebellion, arrives and assumes the reins of government, relieving General Carr, who falls back to second in command. We are all agog to see what will be our new chief's first move. He is fresh from Sheridan's staff in Chicago, and is doubtless primed with latest instructions and wishes of the lieutenant-general. He is no stranger to us, nor we to

him, and his first move is characteristic. At dawn of
day of the 2d, he marches us four miles down stream
to better grass and a point nearer the big trail; sends
Montgomery with his grays to scout over towards
the Black Hills, and Hayes and Bishop with Company "G" to lie along the trail itself—but no Indian
is sighted.

The sun is just rising on the morning of the 3d of
July when my captain, Mason, and I roll out of our
blankets and set about the very simple operations of
a soldier's campaign toilet. The men are grooming
their horses; the tap of the curry-comb and the impatient pawing of hoofs is music in the clear, crisp,
bracing air. Our cook is just announcing breakfast,
and I am eagerly sniffing the aroma of coffee, when
General Merritt's orderly comes running through the
trees. "Colonel Mason, the general directs Company "K" to get out as quickly as possible—Indians
coming up the valley!" "Saddle up, men! lively
now!" is the order. We jump into boots and spurs,
whip the saddles from saplings and stumps, rattle the
bits between the teeth of our excited horses, sling
carbines over shoulder, poke fresh cartridges into revolver chambers, look well to the broad horsehair
"cinches," or girths. The men lead into line, count
fours, mount, and then, without a moment's pause,
"Fours right, trot," is the order, and Mason and I
lead off at a spanking gait, winding through the timber and suddenly shooting out upon the broad, sandy
surface of the dry stream-bed. There the first man
we see is Buffalo Bill, who swings his hat. "This

way, colonel, this way," and away we go on his tracks. "K" is a veteran company. Its soldiers are, with few exceptions, on their second and third enlistments. Its captain ranks all the line officers of the regiment, and admirably commanded it during the war while the field officers were doing duty as generals of volunteers. There is hardly a trace of nervousness even among the newest comers, but this is the first chase of the campaign for us, and all are eager and excited. Horses in rear struggle to rush to the front, and as we sputter out of the sand and strike the grassy slopes beyond the timber belt all break into a lope. Two or three scouts on a ridge five hundred yards ahead are frantically signalling to us, and, bending to the left again, we sweep around towards them, now at a gallop. Mason sternly cautions some of the eager men who are pressing close behind us, and, looking back, I see Sergeant Stauffer's bronzed face lighting up with a grin I used to mark in the old Apache campaigns in Arizona, and the veteran "Kelly" riding, as usual, all over his horse, but desperately bent on being ahead when we reach the scene. Left hands firmly grasp the already foaming reins, while throughout the column carbines are "advanced" in the other.

"Here comes Company 'I,' fellers," is the muttered announcement from the left and rear, and, glancing over my left shoulder, I see Kellogg with his bays and Lieutenant Reilly swinging out along the slope to our left. As we near the ridge and prepare to deploy, excitement is subdued but intense—Buffalo Bill plunging along beside us on a strawberry roan, sixteen

hands high, gets a trifle of a lead, but we go tearing
up the crest in a compact body, reach it, rein up,
amazed and disgusted—not an Indian to be seen for
two miles across the intervening "swale." Away to
the left, towards the Cheyenne, scouts are again excitedly beckoning, and we move rapidly towards them,
but slower now, for Mason will not abuse his horses
for a wild-goose chase. Ten minutes bring us thither.
Kellogg has joined forces with us, and the two companies are trotting in parallel columns. Still no Indian ;
but the scouts are ahead down the valley, and we follow for a brisk half-hour, and find ourselves plunging
through the timber ten miles east of camp. Another
hour and we are dashing along a high ridge parallel
with the Black Hills, and there, sure enough, are Indians, miles ahead, and streaking it for the Powder
River country as fast as their ponies can carry them.
We have galloped thirty miles in a big circle before
catching sight of our chase, and our horses are panting and wearied. Every now and then we pass pack-
saddles with fresh agency provisions, which they had
dropped in their haste. Once our scouts get near
enough to exchange a shot or two, but at last they
fairly beat us out of sight, and we head for home,
reach camp, disgusted and empty-handed, about four
P.M. Two "heavy weights" (Colonel Leib's and
Lieutenant Reilly's) horses drop dead under them,
and the first pursuit of the Fifth is over.

CHAPTER III.

THE FIGHT ON THE WAR BONNET.

THE chase of July 3d, besides killing two and using up a dozen horses, rendered our further presence in the valley of the Cheyenne clearly useless. No more Indians would be apt to come that way when they had the undisturbed choice of several others. General Merritt was prompt to accept the situation, and as prompt to act. Early the next morning, "K" and "I," the two companies engaged in the dash of the day before, took the direct back track up the valley of Old Woman's Fork, guarding the chief and the wagons. General Carr, with companies "B," "G," and "M," marched eastward towards the Black Hills, while Major Upham, with "A," "C," and "D," struck out northwestward up the valley of the Mini Pusa. Both commands were ordered to make a wide *détour*, scout the country for forty-eight hours, and rejoin· headquarters at the head of what was then called Sage Creek. We of the centre column spent the glorious Fourth in a dusty march, and followed it up on the 5th with another.

On the 6th, a courier was sent in to Fort Laramie, seventy miles away, while the regiment camped along the stream to wait for orders. Towards ten o'clock on the following morning, while the camp was principally occupied in fighting flies, a party of the junior officers were returning from a refreshing bath in a deep pool of the stream, when Buffalo Bill came hurriedly towards them from the general's tent. His handsome face wore a look of deep trouble, and he brought us to a halt in stunned, awe-stricken silence with the announcement, " Custer and five companies of the Seventh wiped out of existence. It's no rumor—General Merritt's got the official despatch."

Now we knew that before another fortnight the Fifth would be sent to reinforce General Crook on the Big Horn. Any doubts as to whether a big campaign was imminent were dispelled. Few words were spoken—the camp was stilled in soldierly mourning. That night Lieutenant Hall rode in with later news and letters. He had made the perilous trip from Laramie alone, but confirmed the general impression that we would be speedily ordered in to the line of the North Platte, to march by way of Fetterman to Crook's support. On Wednesday, the 12th, our move began, no orders having been received until the night before. Just what we were to do, probably no one knew but Merritt; he didn't tell, and I never asked questions. Evening found us camping near the Cardinal's Chair at the head of the Niobrara, in a furious storm of thunder, lightning, and rain, which lasted all night, and, wet to the skin, we were glad enough to march off at daybreak on the 13th, and still more glad to camp again that evening under the lee of friendly old Rawhide Peak.

We were now just one long day's march from Fort Laramie, and confidently expected to make it on the following day. At reveille on the 14th, however, a rumor ran through the camp that Merritt had received despatches during the night indicating that there was a grand outbreak among the Indians at the reservation. Of course we knew that they would be vastly excited and encouraged by the intelligence of the Custer massacre. Furthermore, it was well known that there were nearly a thousand of the Cheyennes, the finest warriors and horsemen of the plains, who as yet remained peaceably at the Red Cloud or Spotted Tail Reservations along the White River, but they were eager for a pretext on which to "jump," and now they might be expected to leave in a body at any moment and take to the war-path. Our withdrawal from the Cheyenne River left the favorite route again open, and the road to the Black Hills was again traversed by trains of wagons and large parties of whites on their way to the mines, a sight too tempting for their covetous eyes. Major Jordan, commanding the post of Camp Robinson, had hurriedly described the situation in a despatch to Merritt, and when "Boots and saddles" sounded, and we rode into line, we saw the quartermaster guiding his wagons back over the ridge we had crossed the day before, and in a few minutes were following in their tracks. Away to the east we marched that morning, and at noon were halted where the road connecting Fort Laramie with the reservation crossed the Rawhide Creek. Here Captain Adam with Company

" C " left us and pushed forward to the Niobrara Crossing, twenty-five miles nearer the Indian villages, while
the indefatigable Major Stanton, " our polemical paymaster," was hurried off to Red Cloud, to look into
the situation. The rest of us waited further developments.

On Saturday, the 15th of July, just at noon, General
Merritt received the despatch from the Red Cloud
Agency which decided the subsequent movement of
his command. It led to his first " lightning march "
with his new regiment; it impelled him to a move at
once bold and brilliant. It brought about an utter
rout and discomfiture among the would-be allies of
Sitting Bull, and, while it won him the commendation
of the lieutenant-general, it delayed us a week in
finally reaching Crook, and there was some implied
criticism in remarks afterwards made.

In a mere narrative article there is little scope for
argument. Merritt's information was from Major
Stanton, substantially to the effect that eight hundred
Cheyenne warriors would leave the reservation on
Sunday morning, fully equipped for the war-path, and
with the avowed intention of joining the hostiles in
the Big Horn country. To continue on his march to
Laramie, and let them go, would have been gross, if
not criminal, neglect. To follow by the direct road
to the reservation, sixty-five miles away, would have
been simply to drive them out and hasten their move.
Manifestly there was but one thing to be done: to
throw himself across their path and capture or drive
them back, and to do this he must, relatively speak-

ing, march over three sides of a square while they were traversing the fourth, *and must do it undiscovered.*

If Merritt hesitated ten minutes, his most intimate associates, his staff, did not know it. Leaving a small guard with the wagon train, and ordering Lieutenant Hall to catch up with us at night, the general and seven companies swing into saddle, and at one o'clock are marching up the Rawhide, *away* from the reservation, and with no apparent purpose of interfering in any project, howsoever diabolical, that aboriginal fancy can suggest. We halt a brief half-hour under the Peak, fourteen miles away, water our thirsty horses in the clear, running stream, then remount, and, following our chief, lead away northwestward. By five P.M. we are heading square to the north; at sunset we are descending into the wide valley of the Niobrara, and just at ten P.M. we halt and unsaddle under the tall buttes of the Running Water, close by our old camp at Cardinal's Chair. Only thirty-five miles by the way we came, but horses must eat to live, and we have nothing but the buffalo grass to offer them. We post strong guards and pickets to prevent surprise, and scatter our horses well out over the hillsides to pick up all they can. Captain Hayes and I are detailed as officers of the guard and pickets for the night, and take ourselves off accordingly. At midnight, Lieutenant Hall arrives with his long wagon train. At three A.M., in the starlight, Merritt arouses his men; coffee and bacon are hurriedly served ; the horses get a good breakfast of oats from the wagons,

and at five A.M. we are climbing out of the valley to
the north.   And now, *Messieurs les Cheyennes*, we'll
see who first will bivouac to-night upon the War Bonnet.   You are but twenty-eight miles from it; we
are fifty to the point where your great trail crosses
the little stream.   The Sioux, in their picturesque nomenclature, called it after the gorgeous headpiece of
bead-work, plume and eagles' feathers, they wear in
battle, the prized War Bonnet.   The frontiersman,
scorning the poetic, considers that he has fittingly,
practically, anyway, translated it into Hat Creek, and
even for such a name as this, three insignificant creeks
within a few miles of one another claim precedence—
and Indian and Horsehead creeks are placidly willing
to share it with them.

The sun rises over the broad lands of the Sioux to
the eastward as we leave the shadowy Niobrara behind.   Merritt's swift-stepping gray at the head of
the column keeps us on our mettle to save our distance, and the horses answer gamely to the pressing
knees of their riders.   At 10.15 we sight the palisade fortifications of the infantry company which
guards the spring at the head of old Sage Creek, and
Lieutenant Taylor eagerly welcomes us.   Here, officers, men, and horses take a hurried but substantial
lunch.   We open fresh boxes of ammunition, and
cram belts and pockets until every man is loaded
like a deep-sea diver, and fairly bristles with deadly
missiles.   Then on we go.   East-northeast over the
rolling, treeless prairie, and far to our right and rear
runs the high, rock-faced ridge that shuts out the

cold north winds from the reservation. The day is hot ; we are following the Black Hills road, and the dust rises in heavy clouds above us. But 'tis a long, long way to the Indian crossing, and we *must* be the first to reach it. At sunset a winding belt of green in a distant depression marks the presence of a stream. At eight P.M., silently under the stars, we glide in among the timbers. At nine the seven companies are unsaddled and in bivouac close under the bluffs, where a little plateau, around which the creek sweeps in almost complete circle, forms excellent defensive lair, secure against surprise. We have marched eighty - five miles in thirty - one hours, and here we are, square in their front, ready and eager to dispute with the Cheyennes their crossing on the morrow.

No fires are lighted, except a few tiny blazes in deep - dug holes, whence no betraying flame may escape. Horses and men, we bivouac in a great circle along the steep banks of a sluggish stream. The stars shine brightly overhead, but in the timber the darkness is intense. Mason, my captain, and I are just unstrapping our blankets and preparing for a nap, when Lieutenant Forbush, then adjutant of the regiment, stumbles over a fallen tree, and announces that Company " K " is detailed for guard and picket. I had " been on " all the night before with Captain Hayes, and would gladly have had a sound sleep before the morrow's work ; but when Mason, after reporting for orders to General Merritt, comes back and tells me that I am to have command of the out-

posts to the southeast, the direction from which the
foe must come, there is compensation in the supposed
mistake in the roster.

We grope out in the darkness, and post our pickets in hollows and depressions, where, should the bivouac be approached over the distant ridges, they can
best observe objects against the sky. The men are
tired ; and, as they cannot walk post and keep awake,
the utmost vigilance is enjoined on non-commissioned
officers. Hour after hour I prowl around among the
sentries, giving prompt answer to the muffled challenge that greets me with unvarying watchfulness.
At one o'clock Colonel Mason and I, making the
rounds together, come suddenly upon a post down
among the willows next the stream, and are not
halted ; but we find the sentinel squatting under the
bank, only visible in the starlight, apparently dozing.
Stealing upon him from behind, I seize his carbine,
and the man springs to his feet. Mason sternly re-
bukes him for his negligence, and is disposed to order him under guard ; but old Sergeant Schreiber,
who was never known to neglect a duty in his life,
declares that he and the sentry were in conversation, and watching together some object across the
stream not half a minute before we came upon them.
Everywhere else along our front we find the men
alert and watchful. At three o'clock the morning
grows chilly, and the yelping of the coyotes out over
the prairie is incessant. My orders are to call the
General at half-past three ; and, making my way
through the slumbering groups, I find him rolled in

his blanket at the foot of a big cottonwood, sleeping
" with one eye open," for he is wide awake in an instant, and I return to my outpost towards the southeast.

Outlined against the southern sky is a high ridge,
some two miles away. It sweeps around from our
left front, where it is lost among the undulations of
the prairie. Square to the northeast, some twenty
miles distant, the southernmost masses of the Black
Hills are tumbled up in sharp relief against the dawn.
A faint blush is stealing along the Orient ; the ridge
line grows darker against the brightening sky ; stars
overhead are paling, and the boughs of the cottonwoods
murmur soft response to the stir of the morning
breeze. Objects near at hand no longer baffle our
tired eyes, and the faces of my comrades of the
guard look drawn and wan in the cold light. We are
huddled along a slope which did well enough for night
watching ; but, as the lay of the land becomes more
distinct, we discern, four hundred yards farther out to
the southeast, a little conical mound rising from a
wave of prairie parallel to our front but shutting
off all sight of objects between it and the distant
range of heights, so I move my outpost quickly to
the new position, and there we find unobstructed
view.

To our rear is the line of bluffs that marks the tortuous course of the stream, and the timber itself is
now becoming mistily visible in the morning light.
A faint wreath of fog creeps up from the stagnant
water where busy beavers have checked its flow,

and from the southward not even an Indian eye could tell that close under those bluffs seven companies of veteran cavalry are crouching, ready for a spring.

Turning to the front again, I bring my glasses to bear on the distant ridge, and sweep its face in search of moving objects. Off to the right I can mark the trail down which we came the night before, but not a soul is stirring. At half-past four our horses, saddled and bridled, are cropping the bunches of buffalo grass in the "swale" behind us; the four men of the picket are lying among them, lariat in hand. Corporal Wilkinson and I, prone upon the hill-top, are eagerly scanning the front, when he points quickly to the now plainly lighted ridge, exclaiming:

"Look, lieutenant—there are Indians!"

Another minute, and two miles away we sight another group of five or six mounted warriors. In ten minutes we have seen half a dozen different parties popping up into plain sight, then rapidly scurrying back out of view. At five o'clock they have appeared all along our front for a distance of three miles, but they do not approach nearer. Their movements puzzle me. We do not believe they have seen us. They make no attempt at concealment from our side, but they keep peering over ridges towards the west, and dodging behind slopes that hide them from that direction.

General Merritt has been promptly notified of their appearance, and at 5.15 he and General Carr and two or three of the staff ride out under cover of our position, and, dismounting, crawl up beside us and level their glasses.

"What can they be after? What are they watching?" is the question. The Black Hills road is off there somewhere, but no travel is possible just now, and all trains are warned back at Taylor's camp. At half-past five the mystery is solved. Four miles away to the southwest, to our right front, the white covers of army wagons break upon our astonished view. It must be our indefatigable Quartermaster Hall with our train, and he has been marching all night to reach us. He is guarded by two companies of stalwart infantry, but they are invisible. He has stowed them away in wagons, and is probably only afraid that the Indians won't attack him. Wagon after wagon, the white covers come gleaming into sight far over the rolling prairie, and by this time the ridge is swarming with war-parties of Cheyennes. Here you are, beggarly, treacherous rascals; for years you have eaten of our bread, lived on our bounty. You are well fed, well cared for; you, your pappooses and ponies are fat and independent; but you have heard of the grand revel in blood, scalps, and trophies of your brethren, the Sioux. It is no fight of yours. You have no grievance, but the love of rapine and warfare is the ruling passion, and you must take a hand against the Great Father, whom your treaty binds you to obey and honor. And now you have stuffed your wallets with his rations, your pouches with heavy loads of his best metallic cartridges, all too confidingly supplied you by peace-loving agents, who (for a consid-

3

eration) wouldn't suspect you of warlike designs for
any consideration. You are only a day's march from
the reservation ; and here, you think, are your first
rich victims—a big train going to the Black Hills unguarded. No wonder you circle your swift ponies to
the left in eager signals to your belated brethren to
come on, come on. In half an hour you'll have five
hundred here, and the fate of those teamsters and
that train is sealed.

"Have the men had coffee?" asks General Merritt,
after a leisurely survey. "Yes, sir," is the adjutant's
report. "Then let them saddle up and close in mass
under the bluffs," is the order, and General Carr goes
off to execute it.

The little hill on which we are lying is steep, almost precipitous on its southern slope, washed away
apparently by the torrent that in the rainy season
must come tearing down the long ravine directly
ahead of us ; it leads down from the distant ridge
and sweeps past us to our right, where it is crossed
by the very trail on which we marched in, and along
which, three miles away, the wagon train is now approaching. The two come together like a V, and we
are at its point, while between them juts out a long
spur of hills. The trail cannot be seen from the ravine, and *vice versa*, while we on our point see both.
At the head of the ravine, a mile and a half away,
a party of thirty or forty Indians are scurrying
about in eager and excited motion. "What in thunder are those vagabonds fooling about?" says Buffalo
Bill, who has joined us with Tait and Chips, two of

his pet assistants.   Even while we speculate the answer is plain.   Riding towards us, away ahead of the wagon train, two soldiers come loping along the trail.   They bring despatches to the command, no doubt, and, knowing us to be down here in the bottom somewhere, have started ahead to reach us.   They see no Indians ; for it is only from them and the train the wily foe is concealed, and all unsuspicious of their danger they come jauntily ahead.   Now is the valiant red man's opportunity.   Come on, Brothers Swift Bear, Two Bulls, Bloody Hand ; come on, ten or a dozen of you, my braves — there are only two of the pale-faced dogs, and they shall feel the red man's vengeance forthwith. Come on, come on !   We'll dash down this ravine, a dozen of us, and six to one we'll slay and scalp them without danger to ourselves ; and a hundred to one we will brag about it the rest of our natural lives. Only a mile away come our couriers ; only a mile and a half up the ravine a murderous party of Cheyennes lash their excited ponies into eager gallop, and down they come towards us.

"By Jove ! general," says Buffalo Bill, sliding backwards down the hill, " now's our chance. Let our party mount here out of sight, and we'll cut those fellows off."

"Up with you, then !" is the answer. "Stay where you are, King. Watch them till they are close under you ; then give the word. Come down, every other man of you !"

I am alone on the little mound. Glancing behind me, I see Cody, Tait, and Chips, with five cavalry-

men, eagerly bending forward in their saddles, grasping carbine and rifle, every eye bent upon me in
breathless silence, watching for the signal.   General Merritt and Lieutenants Forbush and Pardee are
crouching below me.   Sergeant Schreiber and Corporal Wilkinson, on all - fours, are half - way down the
northern slope.   Not a horse or man of us visible to
the Indians.   Only my hatless head and the double
field-glass peer over the grassy mound.   Half a mile
away are our couriers, now rapidly approaching.
Now, my Indian friends, what of you?   Oh, what a
stirring picture you make as once more I fix my
glasses on you!   Here, nearly four years after, my
pulses bound as I recall the sight.   Savage warfare
was never more beautiful than in you.   On you come,
your swift, agile ponies springing down the winding
ravine, the rising sun gleaming on your trailing war
bonnets, on silver armlets, necklace, gorget; on brilliant painted shield and beaded legging; on naked
body and beardless face, stained most vivid vermilion.   On you come, lance and rifle, pennon and
feather glistening in the rare morning light, swaying
in the wild grace of your peerless horsemanship;
nearer, till I mark the very ornament on your leader's shield.   And on, too, all unsuspecting, come your
helpless prey.   I hold vengeance in my hand, but not
yet to let it go.   Five seconds too soon, and you can
wheel about and escape us; one second too late, and
my blue-coated couriers are dead men.   On you come,
savage, hungry - eyed, merciless.   Two miles behind
you are your scores of friends, eagerly, applaudingly

watching your exploit. But five hundred yards ahead of you, coolly, vengefully awaiting you are your unseen foes, beating you at your own game, and you are running slap into them. Nearer and nearer — your leader, a gorgeous-looking fellow, on a bounding gray, signals "Close and follow." Three hundred yards more, my buck, and (you fancy) your gleaming knives will tear the scalps of our couriers. Twenty seconds, and you will dash round that point with your war-whoop ringing in their ears. Ha! Lances, is it? You don't want your shots heard back at the train. What will you think of ours? All ready, general?"

"All ready, King. Give the word when you like."

"Not a man but myself knows how near they are. Two hundred yards now, and I can hear the panting of their wiry steeds. A hundred and fifty! That's right—close in, you beggars! Ten seconds more and you are on them! A hundred and twenty-five yards— a hundred—ninety—

"*Now*, lads, in with you!"

Crash go the hoofs! There's a rush, a wild, ringing cheer; then bang, bang, bang! and in a cloud of dust Cody and his men tumble in among them. General Merritt springs up to my side, Corporal Wilkinson to his. Cool as a cucumber, the Indian leader reins in his pony in sweeping circle to the left, ducks on his neck as Wilkinson's bullet whistles by his head; then *under* his pony, and his return shot "zips" close by the general's cheek. Then comes the cry, "Look to the front; look, look!" and, swarm-

ing down the ridge as far as we can see, come dozens
of Indian warriors at top speed to the rescue. "Send
up the first company!" is Merritt's order as he springs
into saddle, and, followed by his adjutant, rides off to
the left and front. I jump for my horse, and the
vagabond, excited by the shots and rush around us,
plunges at his lariat and breaks to the left. As I
catch him, I see Buffalo Bill closing on a superbly ac-
coutred warrior. It is the work of a minute; the Indian has fired and missed. Cody's bullet tears through
the rider's leg, into his pony's heart, and they tumble
in confused heap on the prairie. The Cheyenne struggles to his feet for another shot, but Cody's second
bullet crashes through his brain, and the young chief,
Yellow Hand, drops lifeless in his tracks.

Here comes my company, "K," trotting up from
the bluffs, Colonel Mason at their head, and I take my
place in front of my platoon, as, sweeping over the
ridge, the field lies before us. Directly in front, a
mile away, the redskins are rushing down to join their
comrades; and their triumphant yells change to cries
of warning as Company "K's" blue line shoots up over
the divide.

"Drive them, Mason, but look out for the main
ridge," is the only order we hear; and, without
a word, shout, or shot, "K" goes squarely at the
foe. They fire wildly, wheeling about and backing
off towards the hills; but our men waste no shot,
and we speed up the slope, spreading out uncon-
sciously in open order to right and left. Their bullets whistle harmlessly over our heads, and some of

our young men are eagerly looking for permission to
begin. Now the pursued have opened fire from both
our flanks, for we have spread them open in our rush ;
and, glancing over my shoulder, it is glorious to see
Montgomery's beautiful grays sweeping to our right
and rear, while Kellogg's men are coming "front into
line" at the gallop on our left. We gain the crest
only to find the Indians scattering like chaff before
us, utterly confounded at their unexpected encounter.
Then comes the pursuit—a lively gallop over rolling
prairie, the Indians dropping blankets, rations, everything weighty they could spare except their guns and
ammunition. Right and left, far and near, they scatter into small bands, and go tearing homeward. Once
within the limits of the reservation they are safe,
and we strain every nerve to catch them ; but when
the sun is high in the heavens and noon has come, the
Cheyennes are back under the sheltering wing of
the Indian Bureau, and not one of them can we lay
hands on.

Baffled and astounded, for once in a lifetime beaten
at their own game, their project of joining Sitting
Bull nipped in the bud, they mourn the loss of three
of their best braves slain in sudden attack, and of all
their provender and supplies lost in hurried flight.
Weary enough we reach the agency building at seven
that evening, disappointed at having bagged no greater game ; but our chief is satisfied. Buffalo Bill is
radiant ; his are the honors of the day ; and the Fifth
generally goes to sleep on the ground, well content
with the affair on the War Bonnet.

CHAPTER IV.

THE MARCH TO THE BIG HORN.

CHASING the Cheyennes from the War Bonnet and Indian Creek to the reservation, our seven companies had struck cross country, and until we neared the high bluffs and ridges to the north of the agency, it was not difficult for the wagons to follow us; but it was generally predicted that Lieutenant Hall would never be able to get his train over the ravines and "breaks" which he would encounter on the 18th, and the command was congratulating itself on the prospect of a day's rest at Red Cloud, when at noon, to our utter astonishment, the wagons hove in sight. We had fasted since our four-o'clock breakfast on the previous morning — were hungrily eying the Indian supplies in their plethoric storehouses, and were just about negotiating with the infantry men of Camp Robinson for the loan of rations and the wherewithal to cook the same, when Hall rode in, *nonchalant* as usual, and parked his train of supplies amid shouts of welcome. General Merritt was unfeignedly glad to see his quartermaster; he had received his orders to hasten in to Fort Laramie and proceed to the reinforcement of General Crook, and every moment was precious. We were allowed just two hours to prepare and partake

of an ample dinner, pack our traps and store them in
the wagons again, when "Boots and saddles" was
echoed back from the white crags of Dancer's Hill
and Crow Butte, and at 2.30 we were winding up the
beautiful valley of the White River. Lieutenant
Hall was left with his train to give his teams and
teamsters a needed rest, and ordered to follow us at
early evening.

All the morning the reservation Indians had come
in flocks to have a look at the soldiers who had out-
witted them on the previous day. Arrapahoe and
Ogalalla, Minneconjou and Uncapapa, represented by
dozens of old chiefs and groups of curious and laughing squaws, hung about us for hours — occasionally
asking questions and invariably professing a readiness
to accept any trifle we might feel disposed to part
with. To beg is the one thing of which an Indian
is never ashamed. In Arizona I have known a lot of
Apaches to hang around camp for an entire day, and
when they had coaxed us out of our last plug of tobacco, our only remaining match, and our old clothes,
instead of going home satisfied they would turn to
with reviving energy and beg for the things of all
others for which they had not the faintest use—soap
and writing-paper.

In addition to all the "squaw men" and "blanket
Indians" at the reservation, there came to see us that
day quite a number of Cheyennes, our antagonists of
the day before. Shrouded in their dark-blue blankets
and washed clean of their lurid war-paint, they were
by no means imposing. One and all they wanted to

see Buffalo Bill, and wherever he moved they followed him with awe-filled eyes. He wore the same dress in which he had burst upon them in yesterday's fight, a Mexican costume of black velvet, slashed with scarlet and trimmed with silver buttons and lace—one of his theatrical garbs, in which he had done much execution before the footlights in the States, and which now became of intensified value. Bill had carefully preserved the beautiful war bonnet, shield and decorations, as well as the arms of the young chieftain Yellow Hand, whom he had slain in single combat, and that winter ('76 and '77) was probably the most profitable of his theatrical career. The incidents of the fight of the 17th and the death of Yellow Hand were dramatized for him, and presented one of the most telling of the plays in which he starred all over the East that season. He realized above all expenses some $13,000 on that one alone, and I fancy that some of your readers may have seen it. For a time it was his custom to display the trophies of that fight in some prominent show-window during the day, and take them away only in time for the performance at night. As an advertisement it drew largely in the West, but when Bill reached the refinements of the Middle States and the culture of New England he encountered a storm of abuse from the press and the clergy which, while it induced him to withdraw "the blood-stained trophies of his murderous and cowardly deeds" from the show-windows, so stimulated public curiosity as to materially augment his receipts.

It is in New England, the land of the Pequots and

the Iroquois, that the most violent partisans of the peace policy are to be found to-day. There is method in their cultured mania, for the farther removed the citizen finds himself from the Indian the better he likes him. Year after year, with the westward march of civilization, the Indian has found himself, in the poetic and allegorical language ascribed to him by Cooper and others who never heard him use it, "thrust farther towards the fiery bosom of the setting sun." Each state in turn has elbowed him on towards the Mississippi, and by the time the struggling aborigine was at the safe distance of two or three states away, was virtuously ready to preach fierce denunciation of the people who simply did as it had done. It is comical to-day to hear Mr. Conger, of Michigan, assailing Mr. Belford, of Colorado, because the latter considers it time for the Utes to move or become amenable to the laws of the land; and when we look back and remember how the whole movement was inaugurated by the Pilgrim Fathers, is it not edifying to read the Bostonian tirades against the settlers—the pilgrims and pioneers of the Far West?

Our march to Laramie was without noteworthy incident. We reached the North Platte on Friday afternoon, July 21, spent Saturday in busy preparation, and early Sunday morning, six o'clock, the trumpets were sounding "the General," the universal army signal to strike your tent and march away. The white canvas was folded into the wagons, and in a few moments more the column of horse was moving off on the long-anticipated march to join General Crook.

Captain Egan and Lieutenant Allison of the Second Cavalry rode out from Laramie to wish us godspeed. By eight the sun was scorching our backs and great clouds of dust were rising under our horses' feet, and Laramie was left behind. Many and many a weary march, many a week of privation and suffering, many a stirring scene were we to encounter before once again the hospitable old frontier fort would open its gates to receive us. At half-past two we camped along the Platte at Bull Bend, and had a refreshing bath in its rapid waters; at four a violent storm of wind and rain bore down upon us, and beat upon our canvas during the night, but morning broke all the better for marching. A cold drizzle is far preferable to thick dust. We sped along briskly to the "La Bonté," and from there hastened on to Fetterman, where the main command arrived at noon on the 25th, the wagons and rear guard, of which I was in charge, coming in two hours later, fording the Platte at once, and moving into camp some distance up stream.

Fetterman was crowded with wagon trains, new horses, recruits, and officers, all waiting to go forward to General Crook, north of the Big Horn, and with the eight companies of the Fifth Cavalry as a nucleus, General Merritt organized the array of "unattached" into a disciplined force, brought chaos into prompt subjection, and at eight A.M. on the 26th started the whole mass on its northward march. Among those to meet us here were our old Arizona comrades, Lieutenants Rodgers and Eaton, who had hurried from detached service to catch us, and there were some

FORT FETTERMAN.

comical features in the reunion. They had escaped
from Eastern cities but the week previous, had made
the journey by rail to Cheyenne and Medicine Bow,
and by stage or ambulance to Fetterman, were fresh
and trim and neat as though stepping out for parade.
We had been marching and scouting for six weeks
through scorching dust and alkali, and with untrimmed beards and begrimed attire were unrecognizable.
Rodgers positively refused to believe in the identity
of a comrade whom he had met at a german at
Fort Hays, but forgot his scruples when he received
through that same officer the notification that he was
promoted to the command of Company "A," its captain having suddenly concluded to resign a short time
before.

Here, too, the future medical director of the expedition, Dr. Clements, made his appearance, and joined
for the campaign, and two officers of the Fourth Infantry, whose companies were not included in General
Crook's field force, obtained authority to serve with
the Fifth Cavalry. And among those who cast their
lot with us as volunteers, there came a gallant sailor, a
lieutenant of our navy, who, having leave of absence
from his department after long sea service, came out
to spend a portion thereof in hunting on the Plains,
just as his cousin, Lieutenant Rodgers, was hastening
to join his regiment; and Jack Tar became a cavalry
man, to serve for three months or the war, and it
wasn't a week before Mr. Hunter had won the regard
of every officer and man in the Fifth, and the brevet
of "Commodore," by which title he was universally

hailed throughout the long and dreary campaign that followed.

Two more companies of ours, "E" and "F," had been ordered to join us also, but we were in a hurry, and they followed by forced marches. On the night of the 28th we were encamped in pitchy darkness in a narrow valley at the head-waters of the North Fork of the Mina Pusa. I was aroused from sleep by the voice of Lieutenant Pardee, who was serving as an aide-de-camp to General Merritt, and, rolling out of my blankets, found the general and himself at our tent. They asked if we had heard the distant sound of cavalry trumpets. The general thought he had, and we all went out beyond the post of the sentinels upon the open prairie to listen. It was time for Captains Price and Payne to reach us with their companies, and the general thought that in the thick darkness they had lost the trail and were signalling in hopes of a reply, and so we pricked up our ears. The silence was as dense as the darkness; no sound came from the slumbering camp; no light from the smouldering fire; suddenly there floated through the night air, soft and clear, the faint notes of the cavalry trumpet sounding "Officer's Call;" another minute and it was answered by our chief trumpeter, and, guided by the calls, in half an hour our comrades had joined us, and ten companies of the Fifth Cavalry were camped together for the first time in years.

From that night "Officer's Call" grew to be the conventional signal by which we of the Fifth were wont to herald our coming through the darkness or distance to comrades who might be awaiting us. Last September, when the Utes made their attack on Major Thornburgh's command, your readers will doubtless remember that after that gallant soldier's death the command of the besieged battalion devolved upon Captain Payne, of the Fifth Cavalry. He and his company, who were the first to employ the signal, have best reason to remember its subsequent value, and I cannot do better than to repeat in his own words, my classmate's description of the arrival of General Merritt and the regiment after their famous dash of two hundred miles to the rescue. Of his little battalion of three companies, fifty were lying wounded in the hurriedly constructed rifle-pits, he and his surgeon were of the number, and for six days the Indians had poured in a pitiless fire whenever hand or head became visible. Hoping for the speedy coming of his colonel, Payne tells us: "While lying in the trenches on the night of the 4th of October, this incident came to mind. Believing it *just* possible for General Merritt to reach us next morning, and knowing that, if possible, come he would, I directed one of my trumpeters to be on the alert for the expected signal. And so it was; just as the first gray of the dawn appeared, our listening ears caught the sound of "Officer's Call" breaking the silence of the morning, and filling the valley with the sweetest music we had ever heard. Joyously the reply rang out from our corral, and the men rushing from the rifle-pits made the welkin ring with their glad cheers."

First at the head-waters of the Mina Pusa, in July,

'76; last in the valley of the Milk River. Next? Far
out in the cañons of Colorado, utterly isolated from
the world, snowed in, living we don't know how, four
companies of the Fifth Cavalry are waiting at the
ruins of the White River Agency the result of all this
negotiation in Washington. Merritt with the other
companies, six in number, is wintering at Fort Rus-
sell, on the line of the Union Pacific. More than
probable is it that the earliest spring will find him a
second time making that two-hundred-mile march to
the Milk River, and once again the Rockies will echo
the stirring strains of "Officer's Call."

Saturday, the 29th of July, '76, broke like a morning in mid-Sahara. We marched in glaring sun,
through miles of dust, sage-brush, and alkali, and followed it up on Sunday, the 30th, with just such another; no shade, no grass, no water fit to swallow.
We bivouacked along the Powder River, a curdling
stream the color of dirty chalk, and we gazed with
wistful, burning eyes at the grand peaks of the Big
Horn, mantled with glistening snow, only fifty miles
away. Monday was another day of heat, glare, and
dust, with that tantalizing glory of ice and snow
twenty miles nearer. That night the wind started in
from the west, and blew down from those very peaks,
fanning our fevered cheeks like blessed wavelets from
heaven, as indeed they were. We were gasping for
air on the banks of Crazy Woman's Fork, and would
have suffocated but for that glad relief.

Early next morning Merritt led us on again, marching through a rolling country that became more and

more varied and interesting with every mile; we were edging in closer to the foot-hills of the mountains. Several small herds of buffalo were sighted, and some few officers and men were allowed to go with Cody in chase. At one P.M. we halted on Clear Fork, a beautiful running stream deserving of its name, fresh from the snow peaks on our left; had lunch and rested until five, when once more we saddled up and pushed ahead; came suddenly upon Lake De Smet, wild and picturesque, lying like a mirror in a deep basin of treeless banks, and in a beautiful open glade, rich with abundant green grass and watered by a clear, cold rivulet, we camped in the glorious starlight, thanking Heaven we were out of the desert, and at last along the storied range of the Big Horn.

Wednesday, August 2d, dawned bracing, clear, and beautiful. The glorious sunshine beamed on lofty crags and pine-covered heights close at our left hand, peered into dark ravine and rocky gorge, sparkled on the swift-flowing stream, and on innumerable dew-drops over the glade. Men and horses awoke to new life. A few miles ahead lay a lofty ridge, and from that, said our guides, the valleys of the Tongue and its branches, and the grand sweep of country towards the Rosebud on the north, and the Big Horn River to the northwest, would be spread before us like a map. Over that ridge, somewhere, lies Crook with his force, expectant of our coming; over that ridge, beyond him, are or were ten thousand renegades and hostile Indians, Sioux, and San Arcs, Cheyennes of the North (it was the Southern Cheyennes we whipped back on the War Bonnet), Minne-conjous, Uncapapas (Sitting Bull's Own), Yankton-nais, and Brulés, all banded together in one grand attempt to exterminate the white intruders.

How I envied the advance that day the first glimpse over that divide! But each company took its turn at head of column; and now that we were fairly in among the fastnesses, where attack might be expect-ed at any moment, two companies were daily de-tailed to escort and guard the wagon train, and Com-panies "A" and "K" were the unfortunates to-day. It was mean duty. The road was not bad, but it wound up and down, over crests and through deep ravines. We had to dismount and lend a helping hand half the time. At seven we passed the palisaded ruins of old Fort Phil Kearney, abandoned by "Peace Commis-sion" order in '68; and just beyond we halted and silently surveyed the ridge on which Captains Fet-terman and Brown, Lieutenant Grummond, and three companies of soldiers were slowly slaughtered by Red Cloud and his surrounding thousands in December, '66. We fancied the poor women and children in the fort, listening and looking on in dumb, helpless horror; and then we thought of Custer and his com-rades lying yet unburied only a few miles farther across that uplifted barrier in our front, and then we hurried on, eagerly praying that it might be our fort-une to avenge some of those sacrificed lives; toiled up the long, long ascent, reached the lofty crest, and halted again in sheer amaze. The whole landscape to the north was black with smoke. East, as far as

the Cheetish (Wolf) Mountains ; west, as far as the
Little Horn, from every valley great masses of surging, billowy clouds rolled up to swell the pall that
overspread the northern sky and hung low upon the
dividing ridges towards the Yellowstone. Here and
there forked flames shot up through the heated veil,
and even at our distance we could almost hear their
roar and crackle. "Lo" had set the country afire to
baffle his pursuers, and, knowing of the coming of
Crook's reinforcements, was now, in all probability,
scattering over the continent.

At eleven we passed an abandoned outpost of earth-
works—thrown up, probably, by a detached company
guarding the road. At two we overtook Merritt and
the eight companies resting along a cool, limpid
stream that gave promise of trout; and here we
camped for the night, and listened eagerly to the
news brought us by courier from General Crook.
Scouts were out hunting for the Indians, who had
withdrawn their masses from his immediate front,
and he was only waiting our coming to launch out in
pursuit. We sleep that night restless and impatient
of the delay—morning comes all too slowly—but at
four o'clock we are astir and on the move to meet
our brigadier, but couriers report him coming down
towards us along the main valley of the Tongue. We
unsaddle and wait till three in the afternoon, when
again "the General" sounds, and we march north-
wardly over the ridges towards the thick smoke.
"Crook is camping on Goose Creek," is the explanation, and we are to join him there. At half-

past five we catch glimpses of distant patrols and
herds of cavalry horses and quartermasters' mules
on the sloping side-hills. Presently horsemen come
cantering out to meet us. Gray - haired, handsome,
soldierly as ever, the first to hail us is our old Arizona major, now Lieutenant - Colonel Royall, of the
Third Cavalry—with him a group of his own and the
Second Cavalry officers. But we are still moved on-
ward. We descend a long spur of foot-hill; plunge
through a rapid mountain torrent into dense timber
on the other side, still guided by our welcoming comrades; ride with dripping flanks through willow and
cottonwood into brilliant light beyond. There white
tent and wagon - covers gleam in every direction;
rough, bearded men are shouting greeting; and just
ahead, on the trail, in worn shooting - jacket, slouch
felt hat, and soldier's boots, with ragged beard braided
and tied with tape, with twinkling eyes and half-shy,
embarrassed manner, stands our old Arizona friend
and chieftain, the hardworking soldier we have come
all these many miles to join, looking as natural as
when we last saw him in the spurs of the Sierras.
There is no mistaking the gladness of his welcome.
His face lights up with new light. He has a cordial
word with General Carr, who commands the leading
battalion; then turns to me, and with a grasp of the
hand that fairly makes me wince, gives greeting for
which I'd make that march twice over.

CHAPTER V.

THE ASSEMBLY OF THE B. H. AND Y.

FRIDAY, the 4th of August, 1876, was a busy day in the camp of General Crook. He had been waiting impatiently for the coming of the Fifth Cavalry, in order that he might resume the offensive, and, to use his own words, "finish the campaign in one crushing blow." The tragic success of the Indians on the Little Big Horn, of June 25th, resulting in the annihilation of Custer and five companies of the Seventh Cavalry, compelled General Terry to fall back to the Yellowstone, where he set about the reorganization of his command; and, safely intrenched in his supply camp at the mouth of the Tongue River, he too had been awaiting the arrival of reinforcements. General Miles, with his fine regiment, the Fifth Infantry, was hurried up the Missouri from Fort Leavenworth, and companies of the Twenty-second Infantry, from the Lakes, also hastened to join him. They were stemming the muddy current of the great river as fast as the light-draft steamers could carry them, while we were marching up from Fetterman to join General Crook.

On the 4th of August, Terry's command, consisting of the remnant of the Seventh Cavalry, one battalion

of the Second Cavalry, the Fifth Infantry (Miles),
Seventh Infantry (Gibbon), a battalion of the Twenty-
second, and the Sixth Infantry garrison at Fort Buford, threatened the hostiles on the side of the Yellowstone; while General Crook, with the entire Third
Cavalry, ten companies of the Fifth, and four of the
Second Cavalry, and an admirable infantry command,
consisting of detachments from the Fourth, Ninth,
and Fourteenth regiments, was preparing to advance
upon them from the south. The two armies were
not more than one hundred and twenty - five miles
apart, yet communication between them was impossible. The intervening country swarmed with warriors, six to eight thousand in number, completely
armed, equipped, supplied, and perfectly mounted.
Crook had sallied forth and fought them on the 17th
of June, and found them altogether too strong and
dexterous, so he retired to Goose Creek once more;
and here he lay on the 25th of June, when Custer was
making his attack and meeting his fate — only fifty
miles away, and not a soul of our command had the
faintest idea of what was going on.

Warily watching the two commands, the Indians
lay uneasily between Crook and Terry. Noting the
approach of strong reinforcements to both, they proceeded to get their women and children out of the
way, sending them eastward across Terry's front,
and preparing to do likewise themselves when the
time came for them to start. On the 5th of August
the two armies moved towards each other. On the
10th they met; and one of the most comical sights I

SUPPLY CAMP, HEAD OF TONGUE RIVER.

ever witnessed was this meeting, and one of the most unanswerable questions ever asked was, "Why, where on earth are the Indians?"

However, August the 4th was a day of busy preparation. At ten A.M. the regimental and battalion commanders met in council at General Crook's headquarters, and by noon the result of their deliberations was promulgated. From the reports of his scouts and allies, General Crook had every reason to believe that he would find the mass of Indians posted in strong force somewhere among the bluffs and uplands of the Rosebud, two days' march away to the north. He had been unable to hear from General Terry or to communicate with him. Lieutenant Sibley, of the Second Cavalry, a young officer of great ability, and universally conceded to be as full of cool courage as any man could well be, had made a daring attempt to slip through with thirty picked men; but the Indians detected him quick as a flash, and after a desperate fight he managed to get back to the command with most of his men, but with the loss of all his horses.

The organization of the command was announced at one P.M.: General Crook to command in person, his faithful aide-de-camp, Bourke, to act as adjutant-general, while his staff consisted of Lieutenant Schuyler, Fifth Cavalry, junior aide-de-camp; Dr. B. A. Clements, medical director, assisted by Drs. Hartsuff and Patzki; Major J. V. Furey, chief quartermaster; Captain J. W. Bubb, chief commissary; Major George M. Randall, chief of scouts and Indian allies; and the bloodthirsty paymaster, our old friend Major Stanton, was the general utility man.

The cavalry was organized as a brigade, with General Merritt in command — Lieutenants Forbush and Hall, Fifth Cavalry, Pardee and Young, of the infantry, serving as staff. General Carr took command of the Fifth Cavalry, with myself as adjutant ; and for the first time the promotions which had occurred in the regiment consequent upon the death of General Custer were recognized in the assignments to command. The commissions had not yet been received from Washington, but all knew the advancement had been made. So my old captain, now become Major Mason, turned over Company " K " to its new captain, Woodson, and was detailed to command the Second Battalion of the Fifth Cavalry, consisting of Companies " B," " D," " E," " F," and " K," while the First Battalion—Companies " A," " C," " G," " I," and " M "—remained, as heretofore, under the leadership of our fellow-citizen Major Upham.

The Third Cavalry was commanded by Lieutenant-Colonel Royall, under whom also was the battalion of the Second Cavalry. Consequently, it was his distinguished privilege to issue orders to four battalions, while his senior officer and quondam commander, Lieutenant - Colonel Carr (brevet major-general) had only two. This was a source of much good-natured raillery and mutual chaffing on the part of these two veteran campaigners, and it was Royall's ceaseless delight to come over and talk to Carr about " my brigade," and to patronizingly question him about

" your a—detachment." In fact, I believe that Colonel Royall so far considered his command a brigade organization that his senior major, Colonel Evans, assumed command of the Third Cavalry as well as his own battalion ; but, as this was a matter outside of my own sphere of duties, I cannot make an assertion.

The infantry was a command to be proud of, and Lieutenant-Colonel Alexander Chambers was the man to appreciate it. Detachments from three fine regiments gave him a full battalion of tough, wiry fellows, who had footed it a thousand miles that summer, and we were all the better prepared to march two thousand more.

With every expectation of finding our foes close at hand, General Crook's orders were concise enough. As given to me by General Carr, and recorded in my note-book, I transcribe them here : "All tents, camp equipage, bedding, and baggage, except articles hereinafter specified, to be stored in the wagons, and wagons turned over to care of chief quartermaster by sunrise to-morrow. Each company to have their coffee roasted and ground and turned over to the chief commissary at sunset to-night. Wagons will be left here at camp. A pack-train of mules will accompany each battalion on the march, for the protection of which the battalion will be held responsible. The regiment will march at seven A.M. to-morrow, 'prepared for action,' and company commanders will see to it that each man carries with him on his person one hundred rounds carbine ammunition and four days' rations, overcoat and one blanket on the saddle. Fifty rounds additional per man will be packed on mules. Four extra horses, not to be packed, will be led with each company. Curry - combs and brushes will be left in wagons. *Special instructions for action:* All officers and non-commissioned officers to take constant pains to prevent wastage of ammunition."

That was all. From the general down to sub-alterns the officers started with no more clothing than they had on and the overcoat and blanket indicated in that order. Many, indeed, officers and men, thinking to be back in a week, left overcoats behind, as superfluous in that bright August weather. When I tell you it was ten weeks before we saw those wagons again, meantime the weather having changed from summer sun to mountain storm and sleet, and we having tramped some eight hundred miles, you can fancy what a stylish appearance the Fifth Cavalry—indeed, the whole expedition—presented as it marched into the Black Hills the following September.

Saturday morning, the 5th of August, broke clear and cloudless, and at the very peep of day the hill-sides re-echoed to the stirring music of our reveille. Cavalry trumpet, soft and mellow, replied to the deeper tone of the infantry bugle. We of the Fifth tumbled up in prompt and cheery response to the summons. Roll - call was quickly over. The horses took their final grooming with coltish impatience, and devoured their grain in blissful ignorance of the sufferings in store for them. The officers gathered for the last time in two months around their mess-chests and

thankfully partook of a bountiful breakfast. Then
"the General" rang out from cavalry headquarters;
down fell the snowy canvas in every direction; wagon
after wagon loaded up in the rapid style acquired only
in long campaigning, and trundled off to join the
quartermaster's corral. The long column of infantry crawled away northward over the divide; half a
dozen mounted scouts and rangers cantered away
upon their flanks; the busy packers drove up their
herds of braying mules, lashed boxes of hard-tack
and sacks of bacon upon the snugly-fitting "appa-
rejo"—the only pack-saddle that ever proved a complete success—and finally everything was ready for
the start. The bustling town of yesterday had disappeared, and only long rows of saddles and bridles
disposed upon the turf in front of each company indicated the regimental position.

At General Carr's headquarters, among the willows
close to the stream, a white flag, with a centre square
of red, is fluttering in the breeze. It is one of the signal
flags, but as the regimental standard had been left with
the band at Fort Hays, the general adopted this for the
double purpose of indicating his own position and of
conveying messages to the distant outposts. Yesterday afternoon a group of our Indian allies, Crows and
Shoshones, surrounded that flag with wondering interest from the moment of its first appearance. Accustomed to the use of signals themselves, they eagerly
watch any improvement upon their system, and, learning from Sergeant Center, our standard-bearer and
signal sergeant, that this was a "speaking flag," they

hung around for hours to observe its operation. The
herds of the different companies were browsing on the
hillsides half a mile away, strong pickets being thrown
out in their front, and each herd guarded by a sergeant and party from its own company. So General
Carr, to give the Indians an idea of its use and at the
same time secure more room, directed the sergeant to
" Flag those Second Battalion herds to the other side of
that ravine." So Center signalled "Attention" to the
outposts, to which they waved " 22, 22, 22, 3," the signal for " All right, go ahead, we're ready," and then,
with the staring eyes of a score of swarthy warriors
following his every move, Center rapidly swung his
flag to form the message : "General Carr directs
herds Second Battalion cross ravine." Speedily the
grays of Company " B " and the four bay herds of
the other companies began the movement, were slowly guided through the sorrels, blacks, and bays of
the First Battalion, and commenced the descent into
the ravine. One herd lagged a little behind, and the
general, gazing at them through his binocular, quickly
divined the cause. " Confound that herd guard ; tell
'em to take off those side-lines when they're moving,
if it's only a hundred yards." The message is sent as
given, the side-lines whipped off, the horses step freely
to their new grazing-ground, Crow and Shoshonee mutter guttural approbation and say that flag is " heap
good medicine."

Hours afterwards they are hunting about camp for
old flour-sacks and the like, and several towels, spread
on the bushes at the bathing-place below camp to dry
in the sun, are missing.

Now, on this brilliant Saturday morning, as we wait expectant of the signal "Boots and saddles," the cavalcade of our fierce allies comes spattering and plunging through the stream. Grim old chieftains, with knees hunched up on their ponies' withers, strapping young bucks bedaubed in yellow paint and red, blanketted and busy squaws scurrying around herding the spare ponies, driving the pack animals, "toting" the young, doing all the work in fact. We have hired these hereditary enemies of the Sioux as our savage auxiliaries, "regardless of expense," and now, as they ride along the line, and our irrepressible Mulligans and Flahertys swarm to the fore intent on losing no opportunity for fun and chaff, and the "big Indians" in the lead come grinning and nodding salutations towards the group of officers at headquarters, a general laugh breaks out, for nearly every warrior has decorated himself with a miniature signal flag. Fluttering at the end of his "coup" stick or stuck in his headgear, a small square of white towelling or floursack, with a centre daub of red paint, is displayed to the breeze, and, under his new ensign, Mr. Lo rides complacently along, convinced that he has entered upon his campaign with "good medicine."

Half-past six. Still no signal to bring in the herds. But Merritt, Carr, and Royall are born and bred cavalrymen, and well know the value of every mouthful of the rich dew-laden grass before the march begins. We are exchanging good-byes with the quartermasters and the unhappy creatures who are to remain behind, adding our closing messages to the letters

we leave for dear ones in distant homes, when the
cheery notes ring out from brigade headquarters and
are taken up, repeated along the line by the regimental
trumpeters. Far out on the slopes our horses answer
with eager hoof and neigh; with springy steps the men
hasten out to bridle their steeds, and, vaulting on their
backs, ride in by companies to the line. The bustle of
saddling, the snap of buckle and whip of cinch, suc-
ceeds, then "Lead into line" is heard from the sergeant's
lips. Officers ride slowly along their commands, carefully scrutinizing each horse and man. Blanket, poncho, overcoat, side-line, lariat, and picket-pin, canteen
and haversack, each has its appropriate place and must
be in no other. Each trooper in turn displays his
"thimble belt" and extra pocket package, to show that
he has the prescribed one hundred rounds. The adjutant, riding along the line, receives the report of each
captain and transfers it to his note-book. Away down
the valley we see the Second and Third already in motion, filing off around the bluffs. Then General Carr's
chief trumpeter raises his clarion to his lips. "Mount,"
rings out upon the air, and with the sound twenty
officers and five hundred and fifteen men swing into
saddle. Ten minutes more and we are winding across
the divide towards Prairie Dog Creek on the east.
The Third and Second, a mile to our left, are marching
northeastward on the trail of the infantry. We fill
our lungs with deep draughts of the rare, bracing
mountain breeze, take a last glance at the grand crags
and buttresses of rock to the southward, then with
faces eagerly set towards the rolling smoke-wreaths

that mark the track of the savage foe in the valley of
the "Deje Agie," we close our columns, shake free our
bridle reins, and press steadily forward.   "Our wild
campaign has begun."

CHAPTER VI.

THE MEET ON THE ROSEBUD.

THAT General Crook's command, now designated as
the "Big Horn and Yellowstone Expedition," started
upon its campaign in the best possible spirits and under
favoring skies, no one who saw us that bright August
morning could have doubted.   Unhappily, there was
no one to see, no one to cheer or applaud, and, once
having cut loose from our wagons and their guards,
there was not a soul to mark our progress, unless it
were some lurking scout in distant lair, who trusted to
his intimate knowledge of the country and to his pony's
fleetness to keep himself out of our clutches.   Once
fairly in the valley of the Prairie Dog, we had a good
look at our array.   The Fifth Cavalry in long column
were bringing up the rear on this our first day's march
from Goose Creek ; our packers and their lively little
mules jogging briskly along upon our right flank, while
the space between us and the rolling foot-hills on the left
was thickly covered with our Crow allies.   The Shoshones were ahead somewhere, and we proceeded to
scrape acquaintance with these wild warriors of the
far northwest, whom we were now meeting for the first
time.   Organized in 1855, our regiment had seen its

first Indian service on the broad plains of Texas, and was thoroughly well known among the Comanches, Kiowas, and Lipans when the great war of the rebellion broke out. In those days, with Sidney Johnston, Robert E. Lee, Earl Van Dorn, Kirby Smith, Fitz Hugh Lee, and a dozen others who became notorious in the rebel army as its representative officers, our regiment had been not inaptly styled "Jeff. Davis's Own." But it outgrew the baleful title during the war, and has lost almost every trace of its ante-bellum *personnel.* Two of its most distinguished captains of to-day—Montgomery and "Jack" Hayes—it is true acquired their earliest military experience in its ranks under those very officers. But, while they are all the better as cavalrymen for that fact, they are none the less determined in their loyalty, and both fought in many a wild charge during the rebellion, defending their flag against the very men who had taught them the use of their sabres. In that stern baptism of blood the Fifth became regenerate, and after stirring service in the Army of the Potomac during the war, and throughout the South during reconstruction days, the regiment once more drifted out on the plains, was introduced to the Cheyennes and Sioux in the winter of 1868–9, became very much at home among the Apaches of Arizona from 1871 to 1875, and now we found ourselves, after a long march across country from the Pacific slope, scraping acquaintance with the redoubtable "Crows" of the Yellowstone valley, the life-long enemies of the Sioux.

Riding "at ease," the men talk, laugh, and sing if

they want to.   All that is required is that they shall
not lounge in the saddle, and that they keep accurately
their distance, and ride at a steady walk.   The Crows
are scattered along the entire length of our left flank,
but a band of some fifteen or twenty chiefs and head-
men keep alongside the headquarters party at the front
of column.   There rides General Carr with his adjutant, the surgeon, the non-commissioned staff, and orderlies, and, of course, the standard-bearer, who, as previ-
ously explained, has a signal flag for this campaign,
and it is this which attracts the aborigine.

These Crows are fine-looking warriors, and fine horsemen too; but to see them riding along at ease, their
ponies apparently gliding over the ground in their
quick, cat-like walk, their position in the saddle seems
neither graceful nor secure.   This knot on our left is
full of the most favorable specimens, and they all ride
alike.   Every man's blanket is so disposed that it covers him from the back of his head, folds across his
breast, leaving the arms free play in a manner only an
Indian can accomplish, and then is tucked in about his
thighs and knees so as to give him complete protection.   One or two younger bucks have discarded their
blankets for the day, and ride about in dingy calico
shirts or old cavalry jackets.   One or two also appear
in cavalry trousers instead of the native breech-clout
and legging.   But the moment that Indian dismounts
you notice two points in which he is diametrically opposed to the customs of his white brother: first, that
he mounts and dismounts on the right (off) side of his
horse; second, that he carefully cuts out and throws

5

away that portion of a pair of trousers which with us is regarded as indispensable. He rides hunched up in his saddle, with a stirrup so short that his knees are way out to the front and bent in an acute angle. The stirrup itself is something like the shoe of a lady's side-saddle, and he thrusts his moccasined foot in full length. He carries in his right hand a wooden handle a foot long, to which three or four thongs of deer-skin are attached, and with this scourge-like implement he keeps up an incessant shower of light flaps upon his pony's flank, rarely striking him heavily, and nothing will convince him that under that system the pony will not cover more miles in a day at a walk or lope than any horse in America. His horse equipments are of the most primitive description—a light wooden frame-work or tree, with high, narrow pommel and can-tle, much shorter in the seat than ours, the whole covered with hide, stitched with thongs and fastened on with a horsehair girth, constitute his saddle. Any old piece of blanket or coffee-sack answers for saddle cloth, and his bridle is the simplest thing in the world, a single head-piece, a light snaffle bit, and a rein, sometimes gayly ornamented, completes the arrangement. But at full speed the worst horseman among them will dash up hill or down, through tortuous and rocky stream-beds, everywhere that a goat would go, and he looks upon our boldest rider as a poor specimen.

The Crows are affably disposed to-day, and we have no especial difficulty in fraternizing. Plug tobacco will go a long way as a medium of introduction any-where west of the Missouri, and if you give one Indian

a piece as big as a postage-stamp, the whole tribe will
come in to claim acquaintance. A very pretty tobacco-
pouch of Sioux manufacture which hung always at the
pommel of my saddle, and the heavily beaded buckskin
riding-breeches which I wore, seemed to attract their
notice, and one of them finally managed to communicate through a half-breed interpreter a query as to
whether I had killed the Sioux chief who had owned
them. Finding that I had never killed a Sioux in my
life, the disdainful warrior dropped me as no longer
a desirable acquaintance; and even the fact that the
breeches were a valuable present from no less a hero
than Buffalo Bill failed to make a favorable impression. Following him were a pair of bright-looking
young squaws whose sole occupation in life seemed
to consist in ministering to the various wants of
his sulky chiefship. Riding astride, just as the men
do, these ladies were equally at home on pony-back,
and they "herded" his spare "mounts" and drove
his pack animals with consummate skill. A tiny pappoose hung on the back of one of them, and gazed over
her shoulder with solemn, speculative eyes at the long
files of soldiers on their tall horses. At that tender age
it was in no way compromising his dignity to display
an interest in what was going on around him. Later
in life he would lose caste as a warrior if he ventured
to display wonderment at sight of a flying-machine.
For several hours we rode side by side with our strange
companions. We had no hesitancy in watching them
with eager curiosity, and they were as intent on "picking up points" about us, only they did it furtively.

Gradually we were drawing nearer the swift "Deje Agie," as the Crows call the Tongue River. The valley down which we were moving sank deeper among the bold bluffs on either side. Something impeded the march of the column ahead; the pack trains on our right were "doubling up," and every mule, with that strict attention to business characteristic of the species, had buried its nose in the rich buffalo grass, making up for lost time. "Halt!" and "Dismount!" rang out from the trumpets. Every trooper slips the heavy curb bit from his horse's mouth and leads him right or left off the trail that he may profit by even a moment's rest to crop the fresh bunches in which that herbage grows.

The morning has passed without notable incident. No alarm has come from the scouts in front or flank. We are so far in rear to-day that we miss our friends Cody and Chips, who hitherto were *our* scouts and no one else's. Now they are part and parcel of the squad attached to General Crook's headquarters, of which Major Stanton is the putative chief. We miss our fire-eater of a paymaster—the only one of his corps, I fancy, who would rather undergo the privations of such a campaign and take actual part in its engagements, than sit at a comfortable desk at home and criticise its movements. At noon we come suddenly upon the rushing Tongue, and fording, breast deep, cross to the northern shore. We emerge at the very base of steep rocky heights, push round a ledge that shuts out the northward prospect from our sight, find the river recoiling from a palisade of rock on the east, and tearing back across our

CROOK'S COLUMN ON TONGUE RIVER.

path, ford it again and struggle along under the cliffs on its right bank a few minutes, balancing ourselves, it almost seems, upon a trail barely wide enough for one horseman. What a place for ambuscade or surprise!

We can see no flankers or scouts, but feel confident that our general has not shoved the nose of his column into such a trap without rigid reconnoissance. So we push unconcernedly along. Once more the green, foam-crested torrent sweeps across our line of march from the left, and we ride in, our horses snorting and plunging over the slippery boulders on the bottom, the eager waves dashing up about our knees. Once more we wind around a projecting elbow of bluff, and as the head of our column, which has halted to permit the companies to close up, straightens out in motion again, we enter a beautiful glade. The river, beating in foam against the high, precipitous rocks on the eastern bank, broke in tiny, peaceful wavelets upon the grassy shores and slopes of the western side; the great hills rolled away to the left; groves of timber sprang up in our front, and through their leafy tops the white smoke of many a camp-fire was curling; the horses of the Second and Third, strongly guarded, were already moving out to graze on the foot-hills. An aide-de-camp rides to General Carr with orders to "bivouac right here; we march no further to-day." We ride left into line, unsaddle, and detail our guards. Captain Payne, with Company "F," is assigned the duty of protecting camp from surprise, and he and his men hasten off to surrounding hill-tops and crests from which they can view the approaches, and at two P.M.

we proceed to make ourselves comfortable. We have no huts and only one blanket apiece, but who cares? The August sun is bright and cheery; the air is fresh and clear; the smoke rises, mast-like, high in the skies until it meets the upland breeze that, sweeping down from the Big Horn range behind us, has cleared away the pall of smoke our Indian foes had but yesterday hung before our eyes, and left the valley of the Tongue thus far green and undefiled. We have come but twenty miles, are fresh and vigorous; but the advance reports no signs yet, and Crook halts us so that we may have an early start to-morrow.

We smoke our pipes and doze through the afternoon, stretched at length under the shady trees, and at evening stroll around among the camp-fires, calling on brother officers of other regiments whom we haven't met before in years. But early enough we roll ourselves in our blankets, and, with heads pillowed on turf or saddle, sleep undisturbed till dawn.

August 6th breaks clear and cloudless. Long before the sun can peer in upon us in our deep nook in the valley, we have had our dip in the cold stream, and our steaming and hugely relished breakfast, stowed our tinnikins and pannikins on the pack mules, and wait expectant of "Boots and saddles!" Again the infantry lead the way, and not until seven do we hear the welcome "Mount!" and follow in their tracks. By this time the sun is pouring down upon us; by nine his rays are scorching, and the dust rises in clouds from the crowded trail. The gorge grows deeper and deeper, the bluffs bolder and more precipitous; we can see nothing but precipice on either side, and, lashed and tormented, the Deje Agie winds a tortuous course between. We cross it again and again—each time it grows deeper and stronger. The trail is so crooked we never see more than a quarter of a mile ahead. At noon we overtake the infantry, phlegmatically stripping off shoes, stockings, and all garments " below the belt," for the eleventh time since they left camp, preparatory to another plunge through the stream; and a tall, red-headed Irishman starts a laugh with his quizzical " Fellers, did e'er a one of yez iver cross on a bridge ?"

At two o'clock, after the thirteenth crossing since seven A.M., we again receive orders to halt, unsaddle, and bivouac. Captain Leib and Company "M" mount guard, and with twenty-two miles more to our credit, and with the thick smoke of forest fires drifting overhead, we repeat the performance of yesterday afternoon and night, and wonder when we are to see those Indians.

Reveille and the dawn of the seventh come together. We wake stiff and cold in the keen morning air, but thaw out rapidly under the genial influence of the huge tins of coffee promptly supplied. At six we descry the infantry and the pack trains clambering up the heights to the northwest and disappearing from view over the timbered crests. At seven we again mount and ride down stream a few hundred yards, then turn sharp to the left and up a broad winding ravine along a beaten trail—buffalo and Indian, of great antiquity. Mile after mile we push along up grade—we of the Fifth well to the front to-day and in view of the scouts and advance most of the time. The woods are thick along the slopes, the grass that was rich and abundant in the valley of the Tongue is becoming sparse. Up we go—the ascent seems interminable. Once in a while we catch glimpses of smoke masses overhead and drifting across the face of distant ridges. At last we see knots of horsemen gathering on a high ridge a mile in front; half an hour's active climbing, mostly afoot and leading our horses, brings us close under them. "Halt" is sounded, and General Carr and I go up to join the party on the crest.

We pause on the very summit of the great divide between the Tongue and the Rosebud, and far to south, north, and west the tumbling sea of ravine and upland, valleys that dip out of sight, mountains that are lost in fleecy clouds, all are spread before us. The view is glorious. We look right down into the cañon of the Rosebud, yet it must be six to eight miles away, and how far down we cannot judge. From every valley north and west rolling clouds of smoke rise towards and blacken the heavens. Somewhere over on those opposite bluffs General Crook had his big fight with the Sioux on the 17th of June, but not a Sioux is in sight.

It takes us three good hours to get down into the valley, and here we receive in grim silence the orders to go into bivouac parallel to the stream, facing west. The Indians have burned off every blade of grass their ponies left undevoured along the narrow gorge, and for miles below us the scouts report it even worse. "The whole Sioux nation has been in camp hereabouts not two weeks ago," says one rugged frontiersman, "and I've been nigh onto ten mile down stream and didn't reach the end of the village." The ground is strewn with abandoned lodge-poles, and covered with relics of Indian occupancy too unmistakable to be pleasant.

The Third and Second Cavalry file into position on the eastern bank parallel with our line, and all the pickets go out at once — Captain Hayes, with Company "G," covering our front.

The situation is romantic, but disagreeable. Some of us sleep rather restlessly that night, and one and all welcome the dawn of the 8th. It is more than chilly in the keen morning air, but we march northward in a thick, smoky haze that utterly obscures the landscape. We can see but a short fifty yards in any direction, and the deeper we ride into it the thicker and more suffocating it becomes. Four or five miles down stream, still riding through the lately occupied camps, we bump up against the rear of the column ahead. An aide leads us off to the left, and informs General Carr that there is good grazing in some little breaks and ravines—to unsaddle and give the horses a chance while we wait for reports from the scouts. Here we "loaf" through the entire day, when suddenly the signal to saddle and mount startles us at six P.M., just as we were thinking of going to sleep. We march very rapidly, six, seven, ten miles, and then darkness sets in. Thicker darkness I never encountered. Men pull out their pipes and whiff away at them till the glow of their sparks looks like a long trail of tiny furnace fires, and gives us a clue to fol-

low. No one but an Indian who has lived among these
valleys all his life can be guiding us to-night.   At
nine o'clock the men are singing darky melodies and
Irish songs ; and it is not until 10.30 that we file past
bivouac fires lighted in a deep bend of the stream,
grope our way out to an invisible front, and, fairly
hobbling and half - lariating our horses, throw ourselves down by them to sleep. Captain Rodgers is
notified that he and Company " A " are "for guard ;"
and, for a man who cannot or will not swear, Rodgers manages to express his disgust appropriately.

A slight sprinkling of rain comes on at daybreak,
and we see the infantry hurrying off northward
through the misty light. We soon follow down the
right bank, the Fifth Cavalry leading the column of
horse. Stanton tells us that a large body of Sioux
are not more than four days ahead — were here in
force not four days ago.   It is easy to see that we are
on the trail of an immense number of Indians—eight
to ten thousand — but we judge it to be a fortnight
old. At 9.15 a cold, driving rain sets in, and whirls
in our faces as we march. At two P.M. we bivouac
again, and begin to growl at this will-o'-the-wisp business.   The night, for August, is bitter cold.   Ice
forms on the shallow pools close to shore, and Captain Adam, who commands the guard, declares that
the thermometer was at zero at daybreak. "What
thermometer ?" is the question.   "Vell, any thermometer as was tam fool enough to get here —
un'stand ?" is our veteran's characteristic reply, and
it puts us in better humor. Stiff and cold when we

march at seven o'clock on the 10th, we have not long to suffer from that cause. A bright sun pours down in recompense. We march five miles, halt, and graze awhile ; then push on again along a broad, beaten trail over which countless hordes of ponies must have recently passed. Thick clouds of dust rise high above the bluffs on either side ; the valley opens out wide and rolling east and west. Here the Indian flight has been so rapid that the work of destruction is incomplete, and the grass is excellent in many a spot. "The grandest country in the world for Indian and buffalo now," says General Carr. "Two years hence it will be the grandest place for cattle."

We of the Fifth are marching down the left or western bank of the Rosebud to-day, somewhat independently as regards the rest of the cavalry brigade, which, following the infantry, is away across the valley, close under the slopes and hillsides towards the east. About nine in the morning, while I am profiting by a ten-minute halt to jot in my note-book some of the surrounding topographical features, my orderly and myself climb to the top of the ridge on our left, from which a good view of the country is to be had. Just here the valley runs northeast, and we have been pursuing that general direction for the last day's march ; but right ahead, some two thousand yards, a tall bluff juts out into the valley from the west. The river sweeps round its base in a broad fringe of cottonwoods, and disappears from sight for six or eight miles ; then, over an intervening range, I

see it again, away to the north, making straight for
what must be the valley of the Yellowstone.   Between that great bend of the river and the distant
bluffs on the eastern side, a broad plain, scorched and
blistered by sun and Indian fire, stretches away some
two or three miles in width.   This side of the bend
the slopes gradually near the stream, and the picture
below me is a very pretty one.   Right under our
ridge the Fifth Cavalry, in long column, is just preparing to remount and move on.   A mile away to the
eastward are our brethren of the Second and Third ;
a quarter of a mile ahead of them, the compact battalion of infantry.   Here and there groups of horses,
men, and a fluttering flag indicate the positions in
march of Generals Crook and Merritt.   Half a mile
in advance of all, those little dots of horsemen are our
scouts, while, anyhow and everywhere, in no order
whatsoever, our Crows and Shoshones are scattered
along the column on one flank, while the pack-mules
kick up a thick dust on the other.   The cloud of dust,
in fact, rises from the whole column, and extends way
back up the Rosebud, and even as I am wondering
how far it can be seen, my eye is attracted by just as
thick a cloud around the point, apparently coming up
the valley.   What the mischief can that be?

Answering our eager signals, General Carr comes
hurriedly up the slope and levels his glass.   It is
dust, sure enough, and lots of it.   Nothing but an
immense concourse of four-footed animals could raise
such a cloud.   "Forward !" is the order ; "Indians or
buffalo?" is the query.   "Ride over and report it to

General Merritt," says my colonel to me. So "Donnybrook" strikes a rapid lope, and we pick our way through the cottonwoods, over the stream and up the low bank on the other side, where the first thing that meets my eyes is a grand hullabaloo among the Indians, our allies. They are whooping and yelling, throwing blankets and superfluous clothing to the ground — stripping for a fight, evidently — and darting to and fro in wild excitement. Beyond them the troops are massing in close column behind some low bluffs, and, looking back, I see the Fifth coming rapidly through the stream to join them. Evidently my news is no news to General Merritt ; but the message is delivered all the same, and I get permission to gallop ahead towards the scouts and see what's coming. I make for a bluff just on the edge of the plain I have described, and, nearing it, can see farther and farther around the great bend. Our scouts and Indians are dashing around in circles, and cautiously approaching the turn. Another minute and I have reached the bluff, and there get a grand view of the coming host. Indians ! I should say so — scores of them, darting about in equal excitement to our own. But no Indians are they who keep in close column along that fringe of trees ; no Indians are they whose compact squadrons are moving diagonally out across the broad plain, taking equal intervals, then coming squarely towards us at a rapid trot. Then look ! Each company, as it comes forward, opens out like the fan of practised coquette, and a sheaf of skir

mishers is launched to the front.   Something in the
snap and style of the whole movement stamps them
at once.   There is no need of fluttering guidon and
stirring trumpet-call to identify them ; I know the
Seventh Cavalry at a glance, and swing my old campaign hat in delighted welcome.   Behind them are
the solid regiments of Miles and Gibbon, and long
trains of wagons and supplies.   It is General Terry
and his whole array, and our chiefs ride forward to
greet them.   And then it is that the question is
asked, in comical perplexity, "Why, where on earth
are the Indians ?"   Except our allies, none are in
sight.   They have slipped away between us.

CHAPTER VII.

AWAY TO THE YELLOWSTONE.

NEVER before, and never since, has the valley of
the Rosebud beheld such a gathering as was there to
be seen on that brilliant 10th of August, 1876 —
brilliant, that is to say, as nature could make it, for
in General Crook's command, at least, there was nothing of embellishment.   The war of the Revolution,
the huts of Valley Forge, never exhibited so sombre
an array of soldiery as we presented when General
Terry and his brigade confronted us at the great
bend.

It may be said that we were surprised at the meeting, and it can be established that they were astonished.   Marching up the valley, General Terry was in

daily expectation of finding a mass of Indians in his front. At latest accounts they were in strong force— in thousands, no doubt — between him and General Crook's position at the base of the Big Horn, and he commenced his aggressive move with every precaution, and with supplies for a long and stirring campaign. He had with him a complete wagon train, tents and equipage of every description. We had a few days' bacon and hard-tack, coffee and sugar, and a whole arsenal of ammunition on our mules, but not a tent, and only one blanket apiece. He had artillery in the shape of a few light field-pieces, and was making slow, cautious advances up the Rosebud at the rate of eight or ten miles a day. He had not come upon a single recent Indian "sign," yet knew that the country to the south must have been full of them within the fortnight. So when his scouts reported an immense cloud of dust coming down the valley above the bend, and his Indian allies began the same absurd gyrations and uproar which we had observed in ours, he very naturally supposed that a horde of hostiles was sweeping down to the attack, and made his dispositions accordingly.

It was my good-fortune to be in our advance, and to witness the beautiful deployment of the Seventh Cavalry over the plains in our front, and it is hard to say which side would have whipped if we had not discovered that neither was Sioux. A report gained credence later in the day that Dr. Clements, Crook's medical director, said that it would be Sioux-icidal to fight under the circumstances ; but his friends believed that this eruptiveness was due to professional disappointment at the non-employment of himself and his able assistants, and the matter was hushed up.

Pending the solution of the problem as to the whereabouts of our common foe, the two brigades were ordered to camp at once, and make themselves at home. The generals met and discussed the situation, the scouts made hurried examination of the surrounding country, and the mystery was at an end. Leaving the valley of the Rosebud at the very point where our two commands had confronted each other on the 10th, a broad trail of recent date led away eastward over the divide towards Tongue River. The low hills were stamped into dust by the hoofs of countless ponies. Sitting Bull, Crazy Horse, Spotted Eagle, and the hosts of different kinds of wolves and bears and vultures in which their savage nomenclature rejoices, had fairly given us the slip, and probably ten thousand Indians of various ages and both sexes had swarmed across Terry's long front on the Yellowstone, but beyond the range of his scouts. That a large portion of them would attempt to cross the great rivers farther to the east and escape towards the Canada line was instantly divined, and a prompt man was needed to head a rush back to and then down the Yellowstone to hold the stream and its crossings and check the Indian flight, while our main body pursued along the trail. In less than an hour General Miles had gone to the right about with his regiment and the light guns, and was making long

strides towards the north.   The world has since read
of the tireless energy with which this vigorous soldier has continued the work he commenced that day.
Winter and summer, from one end of the Yellowstone
valley to the other, he has persistently and most successfully hunted the hostiles, until his name has become a synonym for dash and good luck.   Two of
his companies had been stationed with us all the previous winter at Fort Riley, in Kansas, and I was
eager to get over to their camp to see them as soon as
my duties were through ; but long before our horses
were herded out on the foot - hills, and I had seen
Captain Montgomery and Company "B" posted as
our guards, a new column of dust was rising down
the valley, and our Fifth Infantry friends were gone.

The afternoon and evening were spent by the officers of the two commands in pleasant reunion.   We
had nowhere to "receive" and no refreshments to
offer ; so, by tacit agreement, Terry's people became
the hosts, we the guests, and it was fun to mark the
contrast in our appearance.   General Terry, as became a brigadier, was attired in the handsome uniform of his rank ; his staff and his line officers,
though looking eminently serviceable, were all in
neat regimentals, so that shoulder - straps were to be
seen in every direction.   General Crook, as became
an old campaigner and frontiersman, was in a rough
hunting rig, and in all his staff and line there was not
a complete suit of uniform.   Left to our fancy in the
matter, we had fallen back upon our comfortable old
Arizona scouting-suits, and were attired in deerskin,

6

buckskin, flannels, and corduroy ; but in the Fifth Cavalry, you could not have told officer from private.   It may have been suitable as regarded Indian campaigning, but was undeniably slouchy and border-ruffianish. It needed some persuasion to induce old and intimate friends to believe in our identity ; and General Terry's engineer officer and his commissary, who had been chosen "chums" of mine in West Point days, roared with laughter at the metamorphosis.

Their tents were brightly lighted and comfortably furnished.   Even the Seventh Cavalry were housed like Sybarites to our unaccustomed eyes.   "Great guns !" said our new major, almost exploding at a revelation so preposterous.   "Look at Reno's tent— he's got a Brussels carpet !"   But they made us cordially welcome, and were civilly unconscious of our motley attire.

While the chieftains and their staffs discussed the plans for the morrow, we unresponsible juniors contentedly accepted the situation, but by nine P.M. it was known that at early dawn we of Crook's command were to reload our pack-mules with rations from Terry's wagons and continue the pursuit.   Now it began to dawn upon us that we had seen the last of our comforts—our wagons, tents, beds, and clothing— for an indefinite period ; and in Indian warfare particularly, is a stern chase a long chase — unless you have the lead at start.

That night we were bivouacked in the thick underbrush along the Rosebud, hugging the tortuous bends of the stream, and as much as possible keeping our

herds between our lines and the river. Suddenly the
stillness was broken by a snort of terror among the
horses; then a rush as of a mighty whirlwind,
the crash of a thousand hoofs, a shot or two, and
the shouts of excited men, and the herds of Companies "A," "B," and "M" disappeared in a twinkling.
Seized by some sudden and unaccountable panic, they
had snapped their "side lines" like pack-thread, torn
their picket - pins from the loose, powdery soil, and
with one wild dash had cleared the company lines,
and, tracked by the dying thunder of their hoofs,
were fleeing for dear life far to the westward. Officers and men sprang to arms, anticipating attack
from Indians. Many of the First Battalion had been
trampled and bruised in the stampede; but in a moment a dozen experienced campaigners were in saddle
and off in pursuit, and towards morning, after miles
of hard riding, the runaways were skilfully "herded"
back to camp. But the night's adventure cost us the
services of one of our very best officers, as Lieutenant Eaton's pistol was accidentally discharged in the
rush, and tore off a portion of the index finger of his
right hand.

The following morning, August 11th, was by General Crook's people, at least, spent in drawing rations
from the wagons of Terry's command. At ten o'clock
our pack-mules were again loaded up, and by eleven
the Fifth Cavalry were filing eastwardly out of the
valley; marched rapidly on the Indian trail, found the
valley of the Tongue River only nine miles away
across a picturesque divide, descended into a thickly

timbered bottom, marched only a couple of miles
down stream, and there received orders to halt, bivouac again, and were told to wait for Terry's command to join us. We moved into a dense grove of
timber—lofty and corpulent old cottonwoods. Company "D" (Sumner's) posted its guards and pickets,
and the rest of us became interested in the great
quantity of Indian pictures and hieroglyphics on the
trees. We were camping on a favorite "stamping-
ground" of theirs, evidently, for the trees were
barked in every direction for some distance from the
ground, and covered with specimens of aboriginal
art. Sketches of warriors scalping soldiers, carrying
off women on horseback, hunting buffalo, etc., but
with the perceptible preference for the stirring
scenes of soldier fighting. That had become more
popular than ever since the Custer massacre. While
examining these specimens, I was attracted by a shout
and the gathering of a knot of soldiers around some
fallen timber. Joining them, and stepping over the
low barrier of logs, I came upon the body of a white
man, unscalped, who had evidently made a desperate
fight for life, as the ground was covered with the
shells of his cartridges ; but a bullet through the
brain had finally laid him low, and his savage foeman
had left him as he fell, probably a year before we
came upon the spot.

Towards sunset the clouds that had gathered all
day, and sprinkled us early in the afternoon, opened
their flood-gates, and the rain came down in torrents.
We built Indian "wickyups" of saplings and elastic

twigs, threw ponchos and blankets over them, and crawled under ; but 'twas no use. Presently the whole country was flooded, and we built huge fires, huddled around them in the squashy mud, and envied our horses, who really seemed pleased at the change. General Terry and his cavalry and infantry marched past our bivouac early in the evening, went on down stream, and camped somewhere among the timber below. We got through the night, I don't remember how, exactly ; and my note-book is not very full of detail of this and the next four days. We would have been wetter still on the following morning— Saturday, the 12th—if we *could* have been, for it rained too hard to march, and we hugged our camp-fires until one P.M., when it gave signs of letting up a little and we saddled and marched away down the Tongue ten or eleven miles, by which time it was nearly dark, raining harder than ever. General Carr and Mr. Barbour Lathrop (the correspondent of the San Francisco *Call*, who had turned out to be an old acquaintance of some older friends of mine, and whose vivacity was unquenchable, even by such weather as this) made a double wickyup under the only tree there was on the open plain on which we camped for the night, and, seeing what looked to be a little bunch of timber through the mist a few hundred yards away, I went to prospect for a lodging ; found it to be one of the numerous aërial sepulchres of the Sioux, which we had been passing for the last four 'days—evidences that Custer's dying fight was not so utterly one-sided, after all. But, unattractive as this was for a mortal dwelling-place, its partial shelter was already pre-empted, and, like hundreds of others, I made an open night of it.

Sunday morning we pushed on again, wet and bedraggled. No hope of catching the Sioux now, but we couldn't turn back. The valley was filled with the parallel columns — Crook's and Terry's — cavalry and infantry marching side by side. We made frequent halts in the mud and rain ; and during one of these I had a few moments' pleasant chat with General Gibbon, who, as usual, had a host of reminiscences of the grand old Iron Brigade to speak of, and many questions to ask of his Wisconsin comrades. It was the one bright feature of an otherwise dismal day. At 4.30 P.M. the columns are halted for the night, and the cavalry lose not a moment in hunting grass for their horses. Fortunately it is abundant here, and of excellent quality ; and this adds force to the argument that the Indians must have scattered. The scouts still prate of big trails ahead ; but our horses are becoming weak for want of grain, our Indian allies are holding big pow - wows every evening, the Crows still talk war and extermination to the Sioux, but the Shoshones have never been so far away from home in their lives, and begin to weaken. Several of them urge additional reasons indicative of the fact that the ladies of the tribe are not regarded by their lords as above suspicion in times of such prolonged absence. That evening Captains Weir and McDougall, of the Seventh Cavalry, spent an hour or so at our fire, and gave us a detailed account of their

on the 25th, on the Little Big Horn.   They were with
Reno on the bluffs, and had no definite knowledge of
the fate of Custer and his five companies until high
noon on the 27th, when relieved by General Gibbon.
Then they rode at once to the field, and came upon
the remains of their comrades.

   "It must have been a terrible sensation when you
first caught sight of them," said one of their listeners.

   "Well, no," replied McDougall.   "In fact, the
first thought that seemed to strike every man of us,
and the first words spoken were, 'How white they
look !'   We knew what to expect, of course ; and
they had lain there stripped for nearly forty - eight
hours."

   That night the rain continued, and at daybreak on
the 14th the Fifth Cavalry got up and spent an hour
or so in vain attempts at wringing the wet from blanket and overcoat.   By 7.15 we all moved northward
again, though I could see scouts far out on the low
hills on our right flank.   For half an hour we of the
Fifth marched side by side with the Seventh, and our
gaunt horses and ragged - looking riders made but a
poor appearance in such society.   Nearing a ford of
the Tongue River, we found some little crowding and
confusion.   The heads of columns were approaching
the same point upon the bank, and we were just about
hunting for a new ford when the Seventh Cavalry
made a rapid oblique, and Major Reno doffed his
straw hat to General Carr, with the intimation that
we had the "right of way"—a piece of courtesy
which our commander did not fail to acknowledge.

Another ford, from the left bank this time, and before us, coming in from the east, is a valley bounded by low, rolling hills for a few miles, but farther to the eastward we note that high bulwarks of rock are thrown up against the sky. Into this valley we turn ; the grass is good, the water is all too plentiful ; occasional fallen trees in the stream promise fuel in abundance ; but we look somewhat wistfully down the Tongue, for not more than fifteen miles away rolls the Yellowstone. And now once more, as the rain comes down in torrents, we unsaddle, turn our horses out to graze, Kellogg and Company " I " are posted as guards, and we wonder what is going to be done. Only noon, and only ten miles have we come from last camp. Colonel Royall marches his "brigade" farther up stream and follows our example, and then comes over to exchange commiserations with General Carr. The veterans are neither of them in best possible humor. A story is going the rounds about Royall that does us all good, even in that dismal weather. A day or two before, so it was told, Royall ordered one of his battalion commanders to "put that battalion in camp on the other side of the river, facing east." A prominent and well-known characteristic of the subordinate officer referred to was a tendency to split hairs, discuss orders, and, in fine, to make trouble where there was a ghost of a chance of so doing unpunished. Presently the colonel saw that his instructions were not being carried out, and, not being in a mood for indirect action, he put spurs to his horse, dashed through the stream, and reined up alongside the victim with, "Didn't I order you, sir, to put your battalion in camp along the river—facing east?"

"Yes, sir; but this ain't a river. It's only a creek."

"Creek be d—d, sir! It's a river—a river from this time forth, *by order*, sir. Now do as I tell you."

There was no further delay.

All that day and night we lay along Pumpkin Creek. "Squashy Creek" was suggested as a name at once more descriptive and appropriate. The soil was like sponge from the continuous rain. At daybreak it was still raining, and we mounted and rode away eastward—Terry and Crook, cavalry and infantry, pack-mules and all, over an unmistakable Indian trail that soon left the Pumpkin, worked through the "malpais," and carried us finally to the crest of a high, commanding ridge, from which we could see the country in every direction for miles. The rain held up a while—not long enough for us to get dry, but to admit of our looking about and becoming convinced of the desolation of our surroundings. The trail grew narrow and more tortuous, plunged down into a cañon ahead, and as we left the crest I glanced back for a last view of the now distant valley of the Tongue. What it might be in beautiful weather no words of mine would accurately describe, because at such times I have not seen it. What it is in rainy weather no words could describe. And yet it was comfort compared to what was before us.

At noon we were gazing out over the broad valley of Powder River, the Chakadee Wakpa of the Sioux. Below us the Mizpah, flowing from the southwest, made junction with the broader stream, and we, guided by our Indians, forded both above the confluence, and went on down the valley. And so it was for two more days; rain, mud, wet, and cold. Rations were soaked; and we, who had nothing but salt meat and hard-tack, began to note symptoms of scurvy among the men. But we were pushing for supplies now. The Indians had scattered up every valley to the eastward; their pony-tracks led in myriads over the prairie slopes east of the Powder. We could go no farther without sustenance of some kind, and so, on the afternoon of Thursday, the 17th, we toiled down to the valley of the Yellowstone and scattered in bivouac along its ugly, muddy banks. The rain ceased for a while, but not a boat was in sight, no news from home, no mail, no supplies — nothing but dirt and discomfort. We could only submit to the inevitable, and wait.

CHAPTER VIII.

AGAIN ON THE TRAIL.

OUR first impressions of the Yellowstone, as seen from the mouth of the Powder River, were dismal in the last degree; but it was an undoubted case of "any port in a storm." General Terry's supply boat put in a prompt appearance and we drew rations

again on Friday and received intimations that we
might move at any moment. "Which way?" was
the not unnatural question, and "Don't know" the
laconic yet comprehensive answer.

The rain that had deluged us on the march down the
valleys of the Tongue and Powder had ceased from
sheer exhaustion, and we strove to dry our overcoats
and blankets at big fires built in the timber. We had
signalized our meeting with Terry's command by a
royal bonfire which lit up the country by night and
poured a huge column of smoke skywards by day;
but as it was contrary to orders, and a most vivid
indication of our position, Colonel Mason's battalion
received a scathing rebuke for carelessness, and Mason was mad enough to follow the lead of the his-
toric Army of Flanders. A most conscientious and
faithful officer, it seemed to sting him to the quick
that any one of his companies should have been
guilty of such recklessness. So the day after we
reached the Yellowstone, and the horses of the regiments were all grazing out along the prairie slopes
south of camp, and revelling in the rich and plentiful buffalo grass, while all officers and men not on
guard were resting along the banks of the stream,
and growling at the vigorous gale that swept down
from the north and whirled the sand in one's eyes,
there came a sudden shout of fire, and Major Upham
and I, who were trying to make a "wickyup" that
would exclude the wind, became aware of a column
of flame and smoke rolling up in the very centre of
his battalion. In a moment it became evident that

the biggest kind of a prairie fire was started. The men of Company "I" were hurrying their arms and equipments to the windward side, and as one man the rest of the regiment came running to the scene, swinging their saddle-blankets in air.

Fanned by the hurricane blowing at the time, the flames swept over the ground with the force of a blast-furnace; tufts of burning grass were driven before the great surging wave of fire, and, falling far out on the prairie, became the nuclei of new conflagrations. Fire-call was promptly sounded by the chief trumpeter, and repeated along the lines. The distant herds were rapidly moved off to right and left, and hurried in towards the river. The whole command that was in bivouac west of the Powder River turned out to fight the common enemy; but in ten minutes, in all the might of its furious strength, a grand conflagration was sweeping southward towards the rolling hills, and consuming all before it.

Like the great Chicago fire, it started from a cause trivial enough, but, spreading out right and left, it soon had a front of over half a mile, and not till it had run fully two miles to the south was it finally checked. Captain Hayes and a party of old and experienced hands "raced" it far out to the front, and, there setting fire to the grass, extinguishing it from the south and forcing it back against the wind, they succeeded after much hard work in burning off a number of large areas in front of the advancing wall of flame, fought fire with fire, and in two hours were masters of the situation. But most of our grass was gone;

and Saturday afternoon, at four o'clock, we of the Fifth saddled and marched up the Yellowstone in search of fresh pasture. A mile was all we had to go, and moving was no trouble to men who had neither roof nor furniture.

We rode into line in the river bottom again. General Carr, with the headquarters party, seized upon a huge log at least a yard in diameter that lay close to the river brink ; and with this as a backbone we built such rude shelter as could be made with leaves, boughs, and a ragged poncho or two, crawled in and made our beds upon the turf. General Merritt and his staff found shelter in a little grove a few yards away, and with the coming of Sunday morning all had enjoyed a good rest.

Meantime we learned that Buffalo Bill had ridden all alone down towards the Glendive, bent on a scout to ascertain if the Indians were attempting to cross the river. I did not envy him the peril of that sixty-mile jaunt through the Bad Lands, but it was an old story to him. We were to remain in camp to await his report. It seemed that nothing definite had been ascertained as to the movements of the Indians ; and for five days we rested there on the Yellowstone, nothing of interest transpiring, and nothing of especial pleasure.

General Carr, to keep us from rusting, ordered inspection and mounted drills on Sunday and Monday morning ; but then the rain came back, and for forty-eight hours we were fairly afloat. It rained so hard Tuesday and Wednesday nights that the men gave up all idea of sleep, built great fires along the banks, and clustered round them for warmth. Shelter there was none. Some of our officers and men, who had broken down in the severity of the ordeal, were examined by the surgeons, and those who were deemed too sick for service were ordered home on the steamer *Far West*, which would take them by river as far as Bismarck. Among them was Captain Goodloe, of the Twenty-second Infantry, who had been prostrated by a paralytic stroke on the last day's march towards the Yellowstone; and of our own regiment we were forced to part with Lieutenant Eaton, whose severe hurt, received the night of the stampede on the Rosebud, had proved disabling for campaign work. At this time, too, some of our newspaper correspondents concluded that the chances of a big fight were too small to justify their remaining longer with so unlucky an expedition, and the representative of the San Francisco *Call*, and an odd genius who had joined us at Fort Fetterman, and speedily won the sobriquet of "Calamity Jim," concluded that their services would be worth more in some other field.

A great loss to us was in Buffalo Bill, whose theatrical engagements demanded his presence in the East early in the fall; and most reluctantly he, too, was compelled to ask his release. He left his "pardner," Jim White, with us to finish the campaign; and we little thought that those two sworn friends were meeting for the last time on earth when "Buffalo Chips" bade good-bye to Buffalo Bill.

Ten soldiers of the Fifth were pronounced inca-

pacitated by the examiners, and ordered to return.
Among them was an elderly man who had joined the
regiment in June with a good character from the
Fourth Cavalry. The Custer massacre had so preyed
upon his mind as to temporarily destroy his intellect,
or make it too keen for the wits of the Medical Department. I believe that up to the last moment it
was an open question whether Caniff (for such was
his name) was downright insane or only shamming ;
but he carried his point, and got away from the danger he dreaded. "But, Lord, sir," as the corporal in
charge of the detachment afterwards told me, "he
was the sensiblest man you ever see by the time
we got past Bismarck." In fact, it would look as
though that Custer massacre had been responsible for
the unmanning of just three members of the Fifth
Cavalry ; and, to the ineffable disgust of the veteran Company "K," two of them were privates in its
ranks.

Our stay of six days on the Yellowstone presented
no features of general interest. A brace of trading-
boats swept down with the current from the markets
of the Gallatin valley, and some of us were able to
purchase, at fabulous prices, new suits of undercloth-
ing and a quantity of potatoes and onions, of which
the men stood sadly in need. More supplies of grain
and rations arrived, and our horses had a few nibbles
of oats, but not enough to build up any of their lost
strength. General Terry, from the east side of the
Powder, rode over one day to pay a visit to General
Crook ; and the story goes that our brigadier was

pointed out to him squatted on a rock in the Yellowstone, and with that absorbed manner which was his marked characteristic, and a disregard for "style" never before equalled in the history of one of his rank, scrubbing away at his hunting-shirt.

Thursday morning, August the 24th, chilled and soaked, we marched away from the Yellowstone, and mostly on foot, leading our gaunt horses through the thick mud of the slopes along the Powder, we toiled some ten miles; then halted for the night. Then it cleared off, and night came on in cloudless beauty, but sharply cold. Next morning we hung about our fires long after our frugal breakfast, waiting for the signal to saddle and march. Trumpet-calls were forbidden "until further orders;" and it was divined that now, at least, we might hope to see the Indians who had led us this exasperating chase. But it was long before we reached them, and this narrative is running threadbare with dry detail. Let me condense from my note-book the route and incidents of the march to Heart River, where we finally gave up the chase :

"General Terry's cavalry — Seventh and Second — followed us on the march of the 25th, after we had forded Powder River and started up the eastern bank ; camped again that night in the valley after long and muddy march. At seven A.M. on the 26th we of Crook's army cut loose from any base, and marched square to the east ; and General Terry, with his entire command, bade us farewell, and hurried back to the Yellowstone. Couriers had reached him during the night with important information, and he and his people were needed along the crossings of the great river while we hunted the redskins over the prairies. The weather was lovely, the country rolling and picturesque; but far and near the Indians had burned away the grass. Camped on the west fork of O'Fallon's Creek. Game abundant all around us, but no firing allowed." . . . .

"*Sunday,* 27*th.*—Marched seven A.M. at rear of column, north of east; rolling country; no timber; little grass; crossed large branch of O'Fallon's Creek at eleven A.M., where some pack-mules were stalled, but finally got through. Bivouac one P.M. in dry east fork of same creek." . . . .

"*Monday,* 28*th.* — Day beautiful and cool; march rapid and pleasant along the trail on which Terry and Custer came west in May and June. Country beautifully bold and undulating, with fine grass everywhere. We halted on Cabin Creek at 1.30 P.M.; and two hours after, over in the direction of Beaver Creek to the northeast, two large smokes floated up into the still air. Just at sunset there came on a thunder-storm, with rain, hail, and vivid lightning— hailstones as big as acorns, and so plentifully pelting that with great difficulty we restrained our horses from stampede. The lightning kindled the prairie just in front of the pickets, and the rain came only in time to save our grass. Of course, we were drenched with rain and hammered with hail."

"*Tuesday,* 29*th.*—Most beautiful day's march yet;

7

morning lovely after the storm.   We move rapidly
on trail of the infantry, and at ten o'clock are astonished at seeing them massing in close column by di-
vision on the southwest side of grassy slopes that loom
up to a great height, and were soon climbing the
bluffs beyond them — an ascent of some five to six
hundred feet." . . . .

Here General Merritt gave the regiment a lesson
which it richly deserved.   Fuel had been a little
scarce on one or two recent occasions ; and some of
the men, finding a few logs at the foot of the bluffs,
hoisted them on their tottering horses, and were
clambering in this fashion up the ascent, when the
"Chief" caught sight of them.   The general is a
man of great restraint at such a time, but, without the employment of language either profane or
profuse, he managed to convey an intimation to some
eighty acres of hillside, in less than five seconds, that
those logs should be dropped ; and they were.   Later
in the day he devoted a half-hour to the composition
of a general order expressive at once of his views on
the matter which had excited his wrath in the morning, and his intentions with reference to future offend-
ers.   Winding up, as it did, with a scathing denunciation of this "violation of the first principles" of a
cavalryman's creed, we of the Fifth felt sore for a
week after ; but it served us right, and the offence
did not occur again.

We found ourselves on the crest of a magnificent
range, from which we looked down into the beautiful
valley of the Beaver to the east, and southward over

mile after mile of sharp, conical buttes that were utterly unlike anything we had seen before. We had abundant water and grass, and here we rested two days, while our scouts felt their way out towards the Little Missouri.

Thursday, the 31st, with a cold norther blowing, we went down the Beaver ten miles to the north, halted and conducted the bi-monthly muster demanded by the regulations, and again the scouts swept over the country in vain search of Indian signs, while we waited until late the following afternoon for their reports, and then merely moved down the valley another eight miles for the night. On the 2d we put in a good day's work, marching rapidly and steadily until two P.M., still in the beautiful wild valley of the Beaver, catching glimpses during the day of the tall Sentinel Buttes off to our right. Next day we turned square to the east again, jogging quickly along through hills and upland that grew bolder and higher every hour; camped at head of Andrew's Creek; pushed on again on the following morning (Monday, September 4th), cold and shivering in another norther — by nine the rain pouring in torrents. As we neared the Little Missouri the hills became higher, outcroppings of coal were to be seen along every mile. Finally, we *débouched* through a long, deep, tortuous cañon into the Little Missouri itself, forded and bivouacked in a fine grove of timber, where, the rain having ceased again, and with fine, blazing fires in every direction, we spent a night of comfort.

The Indians must be near at hand. The timber, the valley, the fords and crossings, all indicate their recent presence. To-morrow's sun should bring them before our eyes. At daybreak we are up and ready. The day is drizzly, and the command don't seem to care a pin by this time. We are becoming amphibious, and so long as the old cavalryman has a quid of good tobacco to stow in his taciturn jaws he will jog along contentedly for hours, though the rain descend in cataracts.

Our march leads us southeastward up the valley of Davis's Creek—a valley that grows grandly beautiful as we near its head. We of the Fifth are some distance from the head of column as we climb out upon the fine plateau that here stretches for miles from the head of the creek towards the streams that rise a day's march away and flow towards the Missouri. Away in front we can see General Crook and his staff; far out beyond them are tiny dots of horsemen, whom we know to be Stanton and the scouts. Every now and then a deer darts into sight along the column, and now permission is given to shoot; for we are over a hundred miles from the nearest chance for supplies, and have only two days' rations left. We are following those Indians to the bitter end.

Suddenly, away to the front, rapid shots are heard. A moment they sound but a mile distant; in another moment they are dying out of hearing. We prick up our ears and gather reins. Looking back, I see the long column of bearded faces lighting up in eager expectation, but no order comes to hasten our advance.

We hear later that our scouts had succeeded in getting near enough to exchange shots with a small war-party of Sioux; but their ponies were fresh and fleet, our horses weak and jaded, and there was no possibility of catching them.

Late that afternoon we halt at the head of Heart River. And now at last it looks as though we are whipped without a fight. We not only have not caught the Indians, but we have run out of rations. Only forty-eight hours' full supplies are left, but a little recent economizing has helped us to a spare day or so on half-rations. It is hard for us, but hardest of all for the general, and it is plain that he is deeply disappointed. But action is required, and at once. We can easily make Fort Abraham Lincoln in four days; but, by doing so, we leave all the great stretch of country to the south open to the hostiles, and the Black Hills settlements defenceless. Just how long it will take us to march to Deadwood cannot be predicted. It is due south by compass, but over an unknown country. While the chief is deciding, we lie down in the cold and wet and try to make ourselves comfortable. Those who are tired of the campaign and hungry for a dinner predict that the morning will find us striking for the Missouri posts; but those who have served long with General Crook, and believe that there is a hostile Indian between us and the Black Hills, roll into their blankets with the conviction that we will have a fight out of this thing yet.

Many a horse has given out already, and dismounted men are plodding along by the flank of column.

We have been on half-rations for three days, and are
not a little ravenous in consequence, and our campaign
suits, which were shabby on the Rosebud, are rags and
tatters now.   As Colonel Mason and I are "clubbing"
our ponchos and blankets for the night, I turn to my
old captain, with whom it has been my good-fortune
to serve so long and still not to lose him on his
promotion, and ask, "Well, what do you think of
it?"   And Mason, who is an inveterate old growler
around garrison in the piping times of peace, and
stanchest and most loyal of subordinates in trying
times in the field, answers as I could have predicted:
"We oughtn't to give up yet, on account of a little
roughing it; and *Crook's not the man to do it.*"

CHAPTER IX.

THE FIGHT OF THE REAR GUARD.

RAGGED and almost starving, out of rations, out at
elbows and every other exposed angle, out of everything but pluck and ammunition, General Crook gave
up the pursuit of Sitting Bull at the head of Heart
River.   The Indians had scattered in every direction.
We had chased them a month, and were no nearer
than when we started.   Their trail led in as many
different directions as there are degrees in the circle;
they had burned off the grass from the Yellowstone
to the mountains, and our horses were dropping by
scores, starved and exhausted, every day we marched.
There was no help for it, and only one thing left to

do. At daybreak the next morning the orders came, "Make for the Black Hills—due south by compass— seven days' march at least," and we headed our dejected steeds accordingly and shambled off in search of supplies.

Through eleven days of pouring, pitiless rain we plodded on that never-to-be-forgotten trip, and when at last we sighted Bare Butte and halted, exhausted, at the swift-flowing current of the Belle Fourche, three fourths of our cavalry, of the Second, Third, and Fifth regiments, had made the last day's march afoot. One half our horses were broken down for good, one fourth had fallen never to rise again, and dozens had been eaten to keep us, their riders, alive.

Enlivening incidents were few enough, and—except one—of little interest to Milwaukeeans. That one is at your service. On the night of September 7th we were halted near the head-waters of Grand River. Here a force of one hundred and fifty men of the Third Cavalry, with the serviceable horses of that regiment, were pushed ahead under Major Anson Mills, with orders to find the Black Hills, buy up all the supplies he could in Deadwood, and then hurry back to meet us. Two days after, just as we were breaking up our cheerless bivouac of the night, a courier rode in with news that Mills was surrounded by the Indians twenty miles south, and every officer and man of the Fifth Cavalry whose horse had strength enough to trot pushed ahead to the rescue. Through mud, mist, and rain we plunged along, and by half-past ten were exchanging congratulations with Mills and shots with the redskins in as wealthy an Indian village, for its size, as ever we had seen. Custer's guidons and uniforms were the first things that met our eyes—trophies and evidence at once of the part our foe had taken in the bloody battle of the Little Big Horn. Mills had stumbled upon the village before day, made a magnificent dash, and scattered the Indians to the neighboring heights, Slim Buttes by name, and then hung on to his prize like a bull-dog, and in the face of appalling odds, till we rode in to his assistance. That afternoon, reinforced by swarms of warriors, they made a grand rally and spirited attack, but 'twas no use. By that time we had some two thousand to meet them, and the whole Sioux nation couldn't have whipped us. Some four hundred ponies had been captured with the village, and many a fire was lighted and many a suffering stomach gladdened with a welcome change from horse-meat, tough and stringy, to rib roasts of pony, grass-fed, sweet, and succulent. There is no such sauce as starvation.

Next morning, at break of day, General Crook, with the wounded, the Indian prisoners, his sturdy infantry, and all the cavalry but one battalion of the Fifth Regiment, pushed on for the south through the same overhanging pall of dripping mist. They had to go. There wasn't a hard-tack north of Deadwood, and men must eat to live.

The First Battalion of the Fifth he left to burn completely the village with all its robes, furs, and Indian treasures, and to cover the retreat.

As the last of the main column disappeared through

the drizzle, with Mason's skirmishers thrown well out
upon their right flank, a light wind swept upward the
veil of smoke and mist, and the panorama became evident to us and to the surrounding Indians at one and
the same moment. There was no time to take observations—down they came with a rush.

On a little knoll in the centre of the burning village
a group of horsemen has halted—General Carr, who
commands the Fifth Cavalry, his staff and orderlies—
and the first remark as the fog raises falls from the lips
of the adjutant : "By Jove! here's a Badger State
benefit !"

All along the line the attack has commenced and
the battalion is sharply engaged—fighting afoot, their
horses being already led away after the main column,
but within easy call. Our orders are to follow, but to
stand off the Indians. They are not wanted to accompany the march. It is one thing to "stand off the
Indians" and hold your ground—it is quite another to
stand him off and fall back. They are dashing about
on their nimble ponies, following up the line as it dog-
gedly retires from ridge to ridge, far outnumbering
us, and all the time keeping up a rattling fire and a
volley of aboriginal remarks at our expense. "Lo"
yells with unaffected glee when his foe falls back, and
it sometimes sounds not unlike the "yi-i-i-ip" of the
rebels in '63. Along our line there is a business-like
taciturnity, an occasional brief, ringing word of command from some officer, or a half-repressed chuckle of
delight as some Patlander sees an Indian reel in his saddle, and turns to mutter to his neighbor on the skirmish

line that he'd "softened the wax in that boy's ears."
Occasionally, too, some man suddenly drops carbine,
claps his hand to leg, arm, or side, and with an odd
mixture of perplexity and pain in his face looks ap-
pealingly to the nearest officer. Our surgeon is just
bandaging a bullet hole for one such, but finds time
to look-up and ask :

"Why Badger State benefit, King? I don't see the
point."

"Just because there are six Wisconsin men right
here on this slope," is the answer, "and dozens more
for aught I know."

Look at them if you will. I warrant no resident of
the Cream City could recognize his townsmen to-day.
Remember, we've been hunting Sioux and Cheyennes
since May ; haven't seen a shanty for three months,
or a tent for two ; haven't had a change of raiment
for eight weeks, or a shave for ten ; and, under those
battered slouch hats and in that tattered dress, small
wonder that you fail to know the wearers. Right
in our front, half-way to the skirmish line, rides the
major commanding the battalion ; a tall, solidly-built
fellow, with twinkling blue eyes and a bronzed face,
barely visible under the mass of blond hair and beard
over which the rain is dripping. He is a Milwaukeean
and a West-Pointer, a stanch favorite, too ; and to-
day the whole rear guard is his command, and on his
shoulders rests the safety of our move. His is an ugly,
trying duty, but he meets it well. Just now he is
keenly watching the left of his line, and by a trick he
has of hitching forward in his saddle when things

don't go exactly right, you see that something's coming. A quick gesture calls up a young officer who is carelessly lounging on a raw-boned sorrel that sniffs excitedly at the puffs of smoke floating past his nose. Quick as the gesture the officer straightens in his saddle, shifts a quid into his "off" cheek, and reins up beside his commander. The major points to the left and front, and away goes the subaltern at a sputtering gallop. Milwaukee is sending Fond du Lac to make the left company "come down out of that." They have halted on a rocky ridge from which they can gloriously pepper the would-be pursuers, and they don't want to quit. The major is John J. Upham, the subaltern is Lieutenant H. S. Bishop.

Square in front, striding down the opposite slope and up towards us come the Company "G" skirmishers. A minute more and the ridge they have left is swarming with Indians. "Halt!" rings out along the line, and quick as thought the troopers face about, fling themselves *ventre à terre* and blaze away, scattering the Sioux like chaff.

There's a stalwart, bearded fellow commanding the right skirmishers of the company, steadily noting the fire of his men. Never bending himself, he moves from point to point cautioning such "new hands" as are excitedly throwing away their shots. He is their first sergeant, a crack soldier ; Milwaukee, too — for in old days at Engelmann's school we knew him as Johnny Goll. Listen to his captain, half a head taller and quite as prominent and persistent a target, who is shaking a gauntleted fist at his subordinate and shouting, "I've told you to keep down a dozen times, sergeant; now, by God, I want you to do it." This makes the nearest men grin. The others are too busy to hear it.

The scene is picturesque enough from our point of view. To the south, two miles away by this time, Crook's long column is crawling snake-like over the rolling sward. To the west the white crags and boulders of the buttes shut off the view—we are fighting along at their very base. Northward the country rises and falls in alternate grassy ridge and ravine; not a tree in sight—only the low-hanging pall of smoke from the burning village in the near distance; the slopes swarming with dusky horsemen, dashing towards us, whooping, yelling, firing, and retiring, always at speed, except where some practised marksman springs from his pony and prone upon the ground draws bead at our chiefs. Between their restless ranks and us is only the long, thin line of cavalry skirmishers, slowly falling back face to the foe, and giving them gun for gun. Eastward, as far as the eye can reach, the country rolls away in billowy undulations, and—look! there comes a dash of Indians around our right flank. See them sweeping along that ridge? Upham is on low ground at this moment and they are beyond his view, but General Carr sees the attempt to cut us off, and in a second the adjutant of the regiment comes tearing to the line, fast as jaded horse can carry him. A comprehensive gesture accomplishes at once the soldierly salute to the major and points out the new danger. Kellogg's company swings into saddle and fairly springs to the right to meet it.

In buckskin trousers, fringed and beaded, but much the worse for wear, in ragged old hunting-shirt and shapeless hat, none but the initiated would recognize Milwaukee, much less West Point, in that adjutant. But he was marker of our Light Guard years before the war, and the first member of its corps of drummer boys. He is just speeding a grim-looking cavalryman, one of the headquarters orderlies, off with a despatch to General Merritt, and that orderly is a Milwaukeean, too, and may have to "run the gauntlet" getting that message through ; but his face, what you can see of it through grizzled hair and beard, looks unconcerned enough ; and under the weather-stained exterior he is known to be a faithful old soldier—one who loves the rough life better than he did the desk in *ante bellum* days when he was clerking at Hathaway & Belden's. "Old George," as the men call him, ran a train on the Watertown road, too, once upon a time, but about the close of the war he drifted from the volunteers into the regulars, and there he has stuck ever since.

But all this time Crook is marching away faster than we can back and follow him. We have to keep those howling devils beyond range of the main column, absorb their attention, pick up our wounded as we go, and be ready to give the warriors a welcome when they charge.

Kellogg, with Company "I," has driven back the attempted turn of our right, but the Indians keep up

their harassing attack from the rear. Time is precious, and Upham begins to think we are wasting it.
Again the adjutant has come to him from General
Carr, and now is riding along the line to the right,
communicating some order to the officers, while Lieutenant Bishop is doing the same on the left.   Just as
the skirmishers cross the next ridge a few cool old
shots from each company drop on hands and knees,
and, crawling back to the crest, open a rapid fire on
the pursuers, checking them. Covered by this the
main line sweeps down at a run, crosses the low,
boggy ground between them, and toils up the ridge
on which we are stationed. Here they halt, face
about, throw themselves flat on their faces, and the
major signals to the outlying skirmishers to come in ;
they obey with a rush, and a minute after a mass of
Indians pops over the divide in pursuit. With a ringing hurrah of exultation our line lets drive a volley, the
astonished redskins wheel about, those who can, lugging with them the dead or wounded who have fallen,
and scatter off under shelter.

"How's that, King ?" says the major, with a grin.
"Think they've had enough ?" Apparently they
have, as none reappear except in distant groups.
Mount is the word. Ranks are formed, the men chat
and laugh a moment, as girths and stirrups are being
rearranged, then silence and attention as they break
into column and jog off after Crook's distant battalions.

The adjutant is jotting down the list of casualties
in his note-book. "What time is it, major ?" "Eight

o'clock," says Upham, wringing the wet from his hat. "Eight o'clock here; church-time in Milwaukee."

Who would have thought it was Sunday?

CHAPTER X.

"BUFFALO BILL" AND "BUFFALO CHIPS."

In all these years of campaigning, the Fifth Cavalry has had varied and interesting experiences with a class of men of whom much has been written, and whose names, to readers of the dime novel and *New York Weekly* style of literature, were familiar as household words; I mean the "Scouts of the Prairie," as they have been christened. Many a peace-loving citizen and thousands of our boys have been to see Buffalo Bill's thrilling representations on the stage of the scenes of his life of adventure. To such he needs no introduction, and throughout our cavalry he is better known than any general except Crook.

A motley set they are as a class—these scouts; hard riding, hard swearing, hard drinking ordinarily, and not all were of unimpeachable veracity. But there was never a word of doubt or question in the Fifth when Buffalo Bill came up for discussion. He was chief scout of the regiment in Kansas and Nebraska in the campaign of 1868-69, when the hostiles were so completely used up by General Carr. He remained with us as chief scout until the regiment was ordered to Arizona to take its turn at the Apaches in 1871, and nothing but his having a wife and family

prevented his going thither. Five years the regiment
was kept among the rocks and deserts of that marvellous land of cactus and centipede ; but when we came
homeward across the continent and were ordered up
to Cheyenne to take a hand in the Sioux war of 1876,
the first addition to our ranks was Buffalo Bill himself. He was "starring it" with his theatrical troupe
in the far East, and read in the papers that the Fifth
was ordered to the support of General Crook. It was
Bill's benefit night at Wilmington, Delaware. He
rushed through the performance, paid off his company, took the midnight express, and four days later
sprang from the Union Pacific train at Cheyenne, and
was speedily exchanging greetings with an eager group
of his old comrades, reinstated as chief scout of the
regiment.

Of his services during the campaign that followed, a
dozen articles might be written. One of his best plays
is founded on the incidents of our fight of the 17th
of July with the Cheyenne Indians, on the War Bonnet, for it was there he killed the warrior Yellow
Hand, in as plucky a single combat on both sides as
is ever witnessed. The Fifth had a genuine affection for Bill ; he was a tried and true comrade—one
who for cool daring and judgment had no superior.
He was a beautiful horseman, an unrivalled shot, and
as a scout unequalled. We had tried them all—Hualpais and Tontos in Arizona; half-breeds on the great
plains. We had followed Custer's old guide, "California Joe," in Dakota; met handsome Bill Hickox (Wild
Bill) in the Black Hills; trailed for weeks after Crook's

favorite, Frank Gruard, all over the Big Horn and Powder River country; hunted Nez Perces with Cosgrove and his Shoshones among the Yellowstone mountains, and listened to "Captain Jack" Crawford's yarns and rhymes in many a bivouac in the Northwest. They were all noted men in their way, but Bill Cody was the paragon.

This time it is not my purpose to write of him, but, *for* him, of another whom I've not yet named. The last time we met, Cody and I, he asked me to put in print a brief notice of a comrade who was very dear to him, and it shall be done now.

James White was his name; a man little known east of the Missouri, but on the Plains he was Buffalo Bill's shadow. I had met him for the first time at McPherson station in the Platte valley, in 1871, when he came to me with a horse, and the simple introduction that he was a friend of Cody's. Long afterwards we found how true and stanch a friend, for when Cody joined us at Cheyenne as chief scout he brought White with him as assistant, and Bill's recommendation secured his immediate employment.

On many a long day's march after that White rode by my side along the flanks of the column, and I got to know him well. A simpler-minded, gentler frontiersman never lived. He was modesty and courtesy itself, conspicuous mainly because of two or three unusual traits for his class—he never drank, I never heard him swear, and no man ever heard him lie.

For years he had been Cody's faithful follower—half servant, half "pardner." He was Bill's "Fidus

8

Achates;" Bill was his adoration. They had been boys together, and the hero worship of extreme youth was simply intensified in the man. He copied Bill's dress, his gait, his carriage, his speech—everything he could copy; he let his long yellow hair fall low upon his shoulders in wistful imitation of Bill's glossy brown curls. `He took more care of Bill's guns and horses than he did of his own; and so, when he finally claimed, one night at Laramie, the right to be known by some other title than simple Jim White—something descriptive, as it were, of his attachment for Cody and lifelong devotion to his idol "Buffalo Bill," a grim quartermaster (Morton, of the Ninth Infantry), dubbed him "Buffalo Chips," and the name was a fixture.

Poor, honest-hearted "Chips"! His story was a brief one after that episode. We launched out from Laramie on the 22d of June, and, through all the vicissitudes of the campaign that followed, he was always near the Fifth. On the Yellowstone Cody was compelled to bid us a reluctant farewell. He had theatrical engagements to meet in the fall, and about the end of August he started on General Terry's boat for Fort Buford and the States. "Chips" remained in his capacity as scout, though he seemed sorely to miss his "pardner."

It was just two weeks after that we struck the Sioux at Slim Buttes, something of which I told you in a former chapter. You may remember that the Fifth had ridden in haste to the relief of Major Mills, who had surprised the Indians away in our front early Saturday morning, had whipped them in panicky confusion out of their "tepees" into the neighboring rocks, and then had to fight on the defensive against ugly odds until we rode in to the rescue. As the head of our column jogged in among the lodges, and General Carr directed us to keep on down to face the bluffs to the south, Mills pointed to a ravine opening out into the village, with the warning, "Look out for that gully; there are two or three wounded Indians hidden in there, and they've knocked over some of my men."

Everybody was too busy just then to pay much attention to two or three wounded Indians in a hole. We were sure of getting them when wanted. So, placing a couple of sentinels where they could warn stragglers away from its front, we formed line along the south and west of the captured village, and got everything ready to resist the attack we knew they would soon make in full force.

General Crook had arrived on the scene, and, while we were waiting for "Lo" to resume the offensive, some few scouts and packers started in to have a little fun "rousting out them Injuns." Half a dozen soldiers got permission to go over and join in while the rest of us were hungrily hunting about for something to eat. The next thing, we heard a volley from the ravine, and saw the scouts and packers scattering for cover. One soldier held his ground—shot dead. Another moment, and it became apparent that not one or two, but a dozen Indians were crouching somewhere in that narrow gorge, and the move to get them out assumed proportions. Lieutenant Clark, of General Crook's staff, sprang into the entrance, carbine in hand,

and a score of cavalrymen followed, while the scouts and others went cautiously along either bank, peering warily into the cave-like darkness at the head. A squad of newspaper correspondents, led by that reckless Hibernian, Finerty, of the *Chicago Times*, came tearing over, pencil in hand, all eagerness for items, just as a second volley came from the concealed foe, and three more of their assailants dropped, bleeding, in their tracks. Now our people were fairly aroused, and officers and men by dozens hurried to the scene. The misty air rang with shots, and the chances looked bad for those redskins. Just at this moment, as I was running over from the western side, I caught sight of "Chips" on the opposite crest. All alone, he was cautiously making his way, on hands and knees, towards the head of the ravine, where he could look down upon the Indians beneath. As yet he was protected from their fire by the bank itself—his lean form distinctly outlined against the eastern sky. He reached a stunted tree that grew on the very edge of the gorge, and there he halted, brought his rifle close under his shoulder, in readiness to aim, and then raised himself slowly to his feet, lifted his head higher, higher, as he peered over. Suddenly a quick, eager light shone in his face, a sharp movement of his rifle, as though he were about to raise it to the shoulder, when, bang!—a puff of white smoke floated up from the head of the ravine, "Chips" sprang convulsively in the air, clasping his hands to his breast, and with one startled, agonizing cry, "Oh, my God, boys!" plunged heavily forward, on his face, down the slope—shot through the heart.

Two minutes more, what Indians were left alive were prisoners, and that costly experiment at an end. That evening, after the repulse of the grand attack of Roman Nose and Stabber's warriors, and, 'twas said, hundreds of Crazy Horse's band, we buried poor " Chips," with our other dead, in a deep ravine.   Wild Bill, California Joe, and Cosgrove have long since gone to their last account, but, among those who knew them, no scout was more universally mourned than Buffalo Bill's devoted friend, Jim White.

CHAPTER XI.

THE "CHIEF" AND THE STAFF.

WITH the death of our scout, Jim White, that eventful afternoon on the 9th of September, 1876, the skulking Indians in the ravine seemed to have fired their last shot. Several squaws were half dragged, half pushed up the banks, and through them the hidden foe were at last convinced that their lives would be spared if they would come out and surrender.   Pending the negotiations, General Crook himself, with two or three staff officers, came upon the scene, and orders were given that the prisoners should be brought to him.

The time was, in the martial history of our country, when brigadier-generals were as plentiful as treasury-clerks—when our streets were ablaze with brilliant buttons, double rows and grouped in twos; when silver stars shone on many a shoulder, and every such luminary was the centre of half a score of brilliant satellites, the blue-and-gold aides-de-camp, adjutant-generals, etc., etc. But those were the dashing days of the late civil war, when the traditions of 1812 and Mexico were still fresh in the military mind, and when we were half disposed to consider it quite the thing for a general to bedeck himself in all the splendor to be borrowed from plumes, epaulettes, and sashes, and, followed by a curveting train of attendants, to gallop forth and salute his opponent before opening the battle. They did it in 1812, and "Old Fuss and Feathers," as many in the army called Winfield Scott, would have pursued the same system in '47, but for the fact that bluff Zachary Taylor—"Old Rough and Ready"—had taken the initiative, and left all full-dress outfits east of the Rio Grande.

We do things in a still more practical style nowadays, and, when it comes to fighting Indians, all that is ornamental in warfare has been left to them. An Indian of the Sioux or Cheyenne tribe, when he goes into battle, is as gorgeous a creature as vermilion, pigment, plumed war-bonnet, glittering necklace, armlets, bracelets, and painted shield can make him. But here is a chance to see a full-fledged brigadier-general of the United States Army and his brilliant staff in action — date, September 9th, 1876; place, a muddy ravine in far-western Dakota; campaign, the great Sioux war of that year. Now, fellow-citizens, which is brigadier and which is private soldier in this crowd? It has gathered in not unkindly curiosity around three squaws who have just been brought into the presence of the "big white chief."

You are taxpayers—you contribute to the support of the brigadier and the private alike. Presumably, therefore, having paid your money, you take your pick. I see you will need assistance. Very well, then. This utterly unpretending party—this undeniably shabby-looking man in a private soldier's light-blue overcoat, standing ankle-deep in mud in a far-gone pair of private soldier's boots, crowned with a most shocking bad hat, is Brigadier-General George Crook, of the United States Army. He commanded the Eighth Corps at Cedar Creek, and ever since the war closed has been hustled about the great West, doing more hard service and making less fuss about it than you suppose possible in the case of a brigadier-general. He has spent the best days of his life, before and since the war, in the exile of the frontier. He has fought all the tribes on the western slope of the Rockies, and nearly all on the eastern side. Pitt River Indians sent an arrow through him in 1857, and since the day he took command against the Apaches in Arizona no white man's scalp would bring the price his would, even in the most impoverished tribe on the continent.

The rain is dripping from the ragged edge of his old white felt hat and down over his untrimmed beard as he holds out his hand to greet, Indian fashion, the first squaw whom the interpreter, Frank Gruard, is leading forward. Poor, haggard, terrified old wretch, she recognizes the big chief at once, and, springing forward, grasps his hand in both of hers, while her eyes mutely implore protection. Never having seen in all her life any reception but torture for prisoners, she cannot be made to believe, for some minutes, that the white man does not war that way. The other squaws come crowding after her, each eager to grasp the general's hand, and then to insert therein the tiny fist of the pappoose hanging in stolid wonderment on her back. One of the squaws, a young and really handsome woman, is shot through the hand, but she holds it unconcernedly before her, letting the blood drip to the ground while she listens to the interpreter's explanation of the general's assurance of safety.

Standing by the general are two of his aides. West of the Missouri you would not need introduction to him or them, for no men are better known; but it is the rarest thing imaginable to see any one of the three anywhere else. In point of style and attire, they are no better off than their chief. Bourke, the senior aide and adjutant-general of the expedition, is picturesquely gotten up in an old shooting-coat, an indescribable pair of trousers, and a straw hat minus ribbon or binding, a brim ragged as the edge of a saw, and a crown without a thatch. It was midsummer, you recollect, when we started on this raid, and, while the seasons have changed, our garments, perforce, remain the same, what there is left of them.

Schuyler, the junior, is a trifle more "swell" in point of dress. His hat has not quite so many holes; his hunting-shirt of brown canvas has stood the wear and tear of the campaign somewhat better, and the lower man is garbed in a material unsightly but indestructible. All three are old campaigners in every part of the West. The third aide-de-camp we saw in the

previous article, down in the ravine itself, heading
the attack on the Indians.   Clark is unquestionably
the show-figure of the staff, for his suit of Indian-
tanned buckskin seems to defy the elements, and he
looks as handsome and jaunty as the day we met
him on the Yellowstone.

Meantime more Indians are being dragged out of
their improvised rifle-pits—warriors, squaws, and children.   One of the latter is a bright-eyed little miss of
some four or five summers.   She is absolutely pretty,
and looks so wet and cold and hungry that Bourke's
big heart is touched, and, lifting her from the ground,
he starts off with her towards where the Fifth Cavalry
are bivouacked, and I go with them.   The little maid-
en suspects treachery—torture or death, no doubt—
for with all her savage strength she kicks, struggles,
claws, and scratches at the kindly, bearded face, scorns
all the soothing protestations of her captor, and finally,
as we arrive at Bourke's camp-fire, actually tears off
that veteran straw hat, and Bourke, being a bachelor,
hands his prize over to me with the remark that, as a
family man, I may have better luck.   Apparently I do
not, but in a moment the adjutant-general is busying
himself at his haversack.   He produces an almost forgotten luxury—a solid hard-tack ; spreads upon it a
thick layer of wild-currant jam, and hands it to the
little termagant who is deafening me with screams.
"Take it, it's washtay, Wauwataycha;" and, sudden
as sunburst from April cloud, little Wauwataycha's
white teeth gleamed in smiles an instant, and then are
buried in the sweet morsel.   Her troubles are forgot-

ten, she wriggles out of my arms, squats contentedly
in the mud by the fire, finishes a square foot of hard-
tack in less time than we could masticate an inch, and
smilingly looks up for more.

Poor little heathen! It wasn't the treatment she
expected, and, doubtless, more than ever, she thinks
" white man heap fool," but she is none the less happy.
She will fill her own little stomach first, and then go
and tell the glad tidings to her sisters, cousins, and
aunts, and that white chief will have consequential
damages to settle for scores of relatives of the original
claimant of his hospitality. Indian logic in such matters is nothing if not peculiar. Lo argues, " You give
my pappoose something to eat — you my pappoose
friend; now you give me, or you my enemy."

Nothing but big luck will save Bourke's scanty
supply of provender this muddy, rainy afternoon.

We have captured a dozen or more rabid Indians
who but half an hour ago were strewing the hillside
with our dead. Here's one grinning, hand-shaking
vagabond with one of Custer's corporals uniforms on
his back—doubtless that corporal's scalp is somewhere
in the warrior's possession, but he has the deep sagac-
ity not to boast of it; and no man in his sound senses
wants to search the average Indian. They are our
prisoners. Were we theirs, by this time we would be
nakedly ornamenting a solid stake and broiling to a
juicy death to the accompaniment of their exultant
howls. But fate ordains otherwise; we are good
North American citizens and must conciliate—so we
pass them around with smiling, pacific grasp of hand—

cheery "How coolahs," and seat them by the fire and bid them puff of our scanty store of tobacco, and eat of our common stock of pony. But we leave a fair-sized guard with orders to perforate the first redskin that tries to budge, while the rest of us grab our carbines and hurry to our posts. Scattering shots are heard all along and around our line—the trumpets of the cavalry ring out "To arms!" the Fifth Cavalry follows with "Forward." It means business, gentlemen, for here come Crazy Horse, Roman Nose, and scores, nay hundreds, of these Dick Turpins of the Plains, bent on recapturing their comrades. We must drop pen to meet them.

CHAPTER XII.

THE COMBAT OF SLIM BUTTES.

It is a stirring sight that meets the eye as, scrambling up from the shelter of the ravine in which we have been interviewing our captives, we gain the hillside and look hurriedly around. The whole landscape is alive with men and horses in excited motion. We are in a half-amphitheatre of picturesque and towering bluffs. North, south, and west they frown down upon us, their crests enveloped in eddying mist and rain clouds, the sward at their base rolling towards us in successive dips and ridges. Not three hundred yards away the nearest cliff tosses skyward directly south of the centre of the village we have won, but to the west and north they open out a good three-quarter mile away.

The village itself consists of some thirty lodges or tepees of the largest and most ornate description known to Sioux architecture. The prisoners say that the head man of the municipality was Roman Nose, and that he and his band are but flankers of the great chieftain Crazy Horse, whose whereabouts are vaguely indicated as "over there," which may mean among the white crags of Slim Buttes, within rifle shot, or miles away towards the Little Missouri. The tepees are nestled about in three shallow ravines or "cooleys," as the Northern plainsmen sometimes call them, which, uniting in the centre of the metropolis, form a little valley through which their joint contributions trickle away in a muddy streamlet. On a point at the confluence of the two smaller branches stands a large lodge of painted skins, the residence no doubt of some chief or influential citizen, for it is chuck-full of robes and furs and plunder of every description. Here, not inside, for the domicile savors of long and unventilated occupation, but outside in the mud, General Carr has established the headquarters of the Fifth Cavalry. Its left is bivouacked directly in front, facing south in the narrow ravine nearest the tall white butte that stands like a sentinel against the stormy sky, while the rest of the line sweeps around to the west, crossing the level plateau between the two main ravines. Mason's battalion is holding this front and uniting with the Second Cavalry battalion on our right.

Directly behind us rises a mound in the very centre of our position, and here General Merritt, who commands the whole cavalry brigade, has planted his flag. It overlooks the field. Below him to the north are the lodges to which the wounded men have been brought, and where the surgeons are now at work. Here, too, the compact battalion of the infantry has stacked its arms and set about kicking the heavy mud off its worn brogans. Somewhere over there also is the entire Third Cavalry, but I have been too busy with other entertainments since we trotted in at noon to find out much about them. To them belongs solely and entirely the honor of the capture of the village in the first place—only a hundred and fifty men at that. Their advance under Mills and Crawford, Schwatka and poor Von Luettwitz (who pays for the honor with a leg the surgeons have just lopped off) dashed in at daybreak while we were yet twenty miles away, and since we got in to help them hold the prize all hands have had their hands full.

Southeast of Merritt's central position a curling white smoke rising from the main ravine through the moisture-laden air, and begriming the folds of a red-and-blue headquarters flag, indicates where Crook himself is to be found. The brigadier is no better off—cares to be no better off than the private. He has not a rag of canvas to shelter his head.

Close in around the lines the lean, bony, leg-weary horses of the cavalry are herded, each company by itself where best it can find patches of the rich buffalo grass. No need to lariat those horses now. For weeks past they have barely been able to stagger along, and the morning's twenty-mile shuffle through the mud has utterly used them up. Nevertheless, each herd is strongly guarded, for the Indians are lurking all around us, eagerly watching every chance.

The scattering shots from the distant portion of our lines, that have brought us scrambling up the hillside, wake the scene to the instant life and excitement we note as we reach the first ridge. As adjutant, my duties call me at once to General Carr's headquarters, whence half a dozen officers who were gathered in conversation are scattering to their companies. A shout from the hillside announces, "Indians firing into the herds over in front of the Third Cavalry." Even as the hail is heard, a rattling of small arms, the sharp, vicious "ping" of the carbine and the deep "bang" of the longer-ranged rifle, sweeps along the western front. Just as we expected, Crazy Horse has come to the rescue, with all his available warriors. It is just half-past four o'clock by General Carr's watch, and between this and sunset the matter must be settled. As yet we can see nothing of it from our front, but every man seems to know what's coming. "Sound to arms, Bradley," is General Carr's quiet order to our chief trumpeter, and as the ringing notes resound along the ravines the call is taken up from battalion to battalion. The men spring to ranks, the herd guards are hurrying in their startled horses, and the old chargers, scenting Indians and danger, toss their heads snorting in the air and come trotting in to their eager masters. All but one herd—"Look at the Grays," is the cry, for Montgomery's horses have burst into a gallop, excited by the shouts and clamor, and there they go up

the slope, out to the front, and square into the fast-
ness of the Indians. Not yet! A dozen eager troopers, officers and men, have flung themselves on their
steeds, all without saddles, some without bridles, and
are off in chase. No need of their services, though.
That dragoon corporal in charge of the herd is a cool,
practised hand—he *has* to be to wear chevrons in
Montgomery's troop—and, dashing to the front, he half
leads, half turns the leaders over to the left, and in a
great circling sweep of five hundred yards has guided
them back into the very midst of their company. It
is at once skilful and daring. No Indian could have
done it better, and Corporal Clanton is applauded
then and mentioned in General Carr's report there-
after.

Even as it is occurring, the hillsides in our own
front bristle with the savage warriors, too far off as
yet for close shooting, but threateningly near. Our
horses must be kept under cover in the ravines, and
the lines thrown out to meet the foe, so "Forward"
is sounded. Upham's battalion scramble up the ridge
in their front, and the fun begins. All around the
rocky amphitheatre the Indians come bobbing into
sight on their active ponies, darting from behind rocks
and ledges, appearing for a brief instant over the rise
of open ground eight hundred yards away, then as
suddenly dipping out of sight into some intervening
"swale," or depression. The first thing, while the
general's horse and mine are being saddled, is to get
the other animals into the ravine under shelter, and
while I'm at it, Bourke, the aide-de-camp we last saw

petting and feeding his baby-captive, comes rattling
up the pebbly stream-bed and rides out to the front
with that marvellous wreck of a straw hat flapping
about his ears. He never hears the laughing hail of
"How did you leave your baby, John?" but is the
first mounted officer I see along the line.

> " Press where you see my old hat shine,
>   Amid the ranks of war,
>   And be your oriflamme to-day
>   This tile from Omaha."

Macaulay barbarously paraphrased in the mud of Slim
Buttes.

As the general swings into saddle and out to the
front, the skirmish line is spreading out like a fan,
the men running nimbly forward up the ridges. They
are not well in hand, for they fire rapidly as they run.
The volleys sound like a second Spottsylvania, a grand
success as a *feu de joie*, but, as the colonel indignantly
remarks, "They couldn't hit a flock of barns at that
distance, much less an Indian skipping about like a
flea," and orders are sent to stop the wild shooting.
That there are hundreds of Indians is plainly apparent from their rapid fire, but they keep five or six
hundred yards away behind the ridges, peppering at
every exposed point of our line. Upham's battalion
is swinging around to the west ; Mason has pushed
his five companies square out to the front along the
plateau, driving the Indians before him. To his right
the Second and Third Cavalry, fighting dismounted
too, are making merry music. And now, filing over
the ridge, comes the long column of infantry ; and

when they get to work with their "long toms" the Indians will have to skip in earnest. The shrill voice of their gray-bearded old chief sends his skirmishers rapidly out on Upham's left, and a minute more the rocks are ringing with the deeper notes of his musketry. Meantime I have counted at least two hundred and fifty Indian warriors darting down from one single opening among the bluffs square in Mason's front, and the wounded are drifting in from his line far more rapidly than from other exposed points. The brunt of the attack coming along that plateau falls on him and his five companies.

It is growing darker, and the flashes from our guns take a ruddier tinge. The principal occupation of our officers, staff and line, has been to move along among the men and prevent the waste of ammunition. Every now and then some young redskin, ambitious of distinction, will suddenly pop from behind a sheltering hummock and dash at the top of his pony's speed along our front, but over three hundred yards away taunting and blackguarding us in shrill vernacular as he does so. Then the whole brigade wants to let drive at him and squander ammunition at the rate of five dollars a second on that one pestiferous vagabond. "Hold your fire, men!" is the order. "Give them half a chance and some of the painted humbugs will ride in closer."

By 5.30 the light is so uncertain that we, who are facing west along the plateau, and have the grim buttresses of the Buttes in our front, can barely distinguish the scudding forms of the Indians; but the

9

flash of their rifles is incessant, and now that they are
forced back beyond the possibility of harm to our
centre, the orders are to lie down and stand them off.
These men crouching along the ridge are Company
"F," of the Fifth.   They and their captain (Payne)
you-have heard more of in the Ute campaign.   One
of them, a keen shot, has just succeeded in knocking
an Indian out of his saddle and capturing his pony.
and even while his comrades are shouting their congratulations, up comes Jack Finerty, who seeks his items
on the skirmish line, and uses pencil and carbine with
equal facility.   Finerty wants the name of the man
who killed that Indian, and, learning from the eager
voices of the men that it is "Paddy" Nihil, he delightedly heads a new paragraph of his despatch "Nihil Fit," shakes hands with his brother Patlander, and
scurries off to take a hand in the uproar on the left.

> "The war that for a space did fail
>   Now trebly thundering swelled the gale."

Colonel Chambers, with his plucky infantrymen,
has clambered up the cliff on the south, changed
front forward on his right — practically, not tacti-
cally—and got in a flank fire along the very depressions in which the Indians are settled.   This is more
than they can stand.   The sun goes down at Slim
Buttes on hundreds of baffled and discomfited Sioux.
They have lost their village ; lost three hundred tip-
top ponies.   A dozen of their warriors and squaws
are in our hands, and a dozen more are dead and dying in the attempt to recapture them ; and the big

white chief Crook has managed to gain all this with starving men and skeleton horses.

Drawing in for the night, we post strong pickets well out in every direction, but they are undisturbed. Now comes the summing-up of casualties. The adjutants make the weary round of their regiments through wind and rain, taking the reports of company commanders, and then repairing to the surgeons to verify the lists. Two or three lodges have been converted into field hospitals ; and in one of these, among our own wounded, two of the surgeons are turning their attention to a captive—the warrior American Horse. He lies upon some muddy robes, with the life-blood ebbing from a ghastly hole in his side. Dr. Clements examines his savage patient tenderly, gently as he would a child ; and, though he sees that nothing can save life, he does all that art can suggest. It is a painful task to both surgeon and subject. The latter scorns chloroform, and mutters some order to a squaw crouching at his feet. She glides silently from the tepee, and returns with a bit of hard stick ; this he thrusts between his teeth, and then, as the surgeons work, and the sweat of agony breaks out upon his forehead, he bites deep into the wood, but never groans nor shrinks. Before the dawn his fierce spirit has taken its flight, and the squaws are crooning the death-chant by his side.

Our own dead are fortunately few, and they are buried deep in the ravine before we move southward in the morning—not only buried deep, but a thousand horses, in column of twos, tramp over the new-made graves and obliterate the trace. You think this is but poor respect to show to a soldier's grave, no doubt ; but then you don't know Indians, and cannot be expected to know that as soon as we are gone the skulking rascals will come prowling into the camp, hunting high and low for those graves, and, if they find them, will dig up the bodies we would honor, secure the scalps as trophies of their prowess, and then, after indescribable hackings and mutilations, consign the poor remains to their four - footed relatives, the prairie wolves.

Our wounded are many, and a hard time the patient fellows are having. Such rude shelter as their comrades can improvise from the Indian tepees we interpose between them and the dripping skies above. The rain - drops sputter in the flickering watch - fires around their cheerless bivouac ; the night wind stirs the moaning pines upon the cliffs, and sweeps down in chill discordance through creaking lodge - poles and flapping roof of hide ; the gaunt horses huddle close for warmth and shelter ; the muffled challenge of the outlying picket is answered by the yelp of skulking coyote ; and wet, cold, muddy, and, oh ! so hungry, the victors hug their drenched blankets about their ears, and, grasping their carbines, pillowed on their saddles, sleep the sleep of the deserving.

CHAPTER XIII.

A RACE FOR RATIONS.

THE village of Slim Buttes destroyed, General Crook pushed ahead on his southward march in search of the Black Hills and rations. All Sunday morning Upham's battalion of the Fifth Cavalry covered the rear, and fought back the savage attacks upon the column ; but, once well away from the smoking ruins, we were but little molested, and soon after noon caught up with the rest of the regiment, and found the entire command going into bivouac along a little stream flowing northward from an opening among towering cliffs that were thrown like a barrier athwart our line of march. It was cold, cheerless, rainy weather, but here we found grass and water for our famished cattle ; plenty of timber for our fires, though we had not a thing to cook, but men and horses were weak and chilled, and glad of a chance to rest.

Here Doctors Clements, Hartsuff, and Patzki, with their assistants, went busily to work perfecting the improvised transportation for the wounded. There was not an ambulance or a field-litter in the command. Two officers — Bache, of the Fifth, and Von Luettwitz, of the Third Cavalry — were utterly *hors du combat*, the latter having left his leg at the fight on the previous day, and some twenty-five men, more or less severely wounded, were unable either to walk or ride a horse.

Frontiersmen are quick to take lessons from the Indians, the most practical of transportation masters. Saplings twelve feet in length were cut (Indian lodge-poles were utilized) ; the slender ends of two of these were lashed securely on either side of a spare pack-mule, the heavy ends trailing along the ground, and fastened some three feet apart by cross-bars. Canvas and blankets were stretched across the space between ; hereon one wounded man was laid, and what the Indians and plainsmen call a *travois* was complete.   Over prairie or rockless road it does very well, but for the severely wounded a far more comfortable litter was devised.   Two mules were lashed "fore and aft " between two longer saplings ; the intervening space was rudely but comfortably upholstered with robes and blankets, and therein the invalid might ride for hours as smoothly as in a palace car.   Once, in the Arizona mountains, I was carried an entire week in a similar contrivance, and never enjoyed easier locomotion — so long as the mules behaved.   But just here it may be remarked that comfort which is in the faintest degree dependent upon the uniform and steadfast serenity of the army mule is of most uncertain tenure.   Poor McKinstry, our wagon-master (who was killed in Payne's fight with the Utes last September, and whose unflattering comparison may have been provoked by unhappy experiences with the sex), used to say : " Most mules could

A SICK SOLDIER ON A "TRAVOIS."

swap ends quicker'n a woman could change her
mind ;" and it was by no means required that the
mule should " swap ends " to render the situation of
the poor fellow in the *travois* undesirable, if, indeed,
he was permitted to retain it.

Sunday afternoon was spent in doing the little that
could be done towards making the wounded comfortable, and the manufacture of rude leggins, moccasins,
etc., from the skins captured from the Indians on the
previous day.   Sharp lookouts were kept, but no enemy appeared.   Evidently the Sioux were more than
satisfied that Crook was worse than a badger in a bar-
rel—a bad one to tackle.

Early on the morning of the 11th we climbed
stiffly into saddle, and pushed on after our chief.
Our way for some two miles or more led up grade
through wooded bluffs and heights.   A dense fog
hung low upon the landscape, and we could only follow blindly in the trail of our leaders.   It was part
of my duty to record each day's progress, and to
sketch in my note - book the topography of the line
of march.   A compass was always in the cuff of
my gauntlet, and note - book in the breast of my
hunting-shirt, but for three or four days only the
trail itself, with streams we crossed and the heights
within a mile or two of the flank, had been jotted
down.   Nothing further could be seen.   It rained
eleven days and nights without perceptible stop, and
the whole country was flooded—so far as the mist
would let us judge.

But this wretched Monday morning, an hour out

from bivouac, we came upon a view I never shall forget. Riding along in the Fifth Cavalry column—every man wrapped in his own thoughts, and wishing himself wrapped in something warmer, all too cold and wet and dispirited to talk—we were aroused by exclamations of surprise and wonder among the troopers ahead. A moment more and we arrived in amaze at a veritable jumping-off place, a sheer precipice, and I reined out to the right to dismount and jot down the situation. We had been winding along up, up, for over an hour, following some old Indian trail that seemed to lead to the moon, and all of a sudden had come apparently to the end of the world. General Crook, his staff and escort, the dismounted men and the infantry battalion away ahead had turned sharp to the left, and could be faintly seen winding off into cloud-land some three hundred feet below. Directly in our front, to the south, rolling, eddying masses of fog were the only visible features. We were standing on the brink of a vertical cliff, its base lost in clouds far beneath. Here and there a faint breeze tore rents through the misty veil, and we caught glimpses of a treeless, shrubless plain beneath. Soon there came sturdier puffs of air; the sun somewhere aloft was shining brightly. We could neither see nor feel it—had begun to lose faith in its existence—but the clouds yielded to its force, and, swayed by the rising wind, drew away upward. Divested of the glow of colored fires, the glare of calcium light, the shimmering, spangled radiance of the stage, the symphony of sweet orchestra, we were treated to a transformation scene the like of which I have never witnessed, and never want to see again.

The first curtain of fog uplifting, revealed rolling away five hundred feet beneath a brown barren, that ghastly compound of spongy ashes, yielding sand, and soilless, soulless earth, on which even greasewood cannot grow, and sage - brush sickens and dies — the "*mauvaises terres*" of the French missionaries and fur-traders—the curt "bad lands" of the Plains vernacular, the meanest country under the sun. A second curtain, rising farther away to the slow music of muttered profanity from the audience, revealed only worse and more of it. The third curtain exposed the same rolling barren miles to the southward. The fourth reached away to the very horizon, and vouchsafed not a glimpse of the longed-for Hills, nor a sign of the needed succor. Hope died from hungry eyes, and strong men turned away with stifled groans.

One or two of us there were who knew that, long before we got sight of the Black Hills, we must pass the Sioux landmark of "Deer's Ears"—twin conical heights that could be seen for miles in every direction, and even they were beyond range of my field-glasses. My poor horse, ugly, raw - boned, starved, but faithful "Blatherskite," was it in wretched premonition of your fate, I wonder, that you added your equine groan to the human chorus? You and your partner, "Donnybrook," were ugly enough when I picked you out of the quartermaster's herd at Fort Hays the night we made our sudden start for the

Sioux campaign. You had little to recommend you beyond the facility with which you could rattle your heels like shillalahs about the ribs of your companions—a trait which led to your Celtic titles—but you never thought so poorly of your rider as to suppose that, after you had worn yourselves down to skin and bone in carrying him those bleak two thousand miles, he would help eat you ; but he did—and it seemed like cannibalism.

Well! The story of that day's march isn't worth the telling. We went afoot, dragging pounds of mud with every step, and towing our wretched steeds by the bridle-rein ; envying the gaunt infantry, who had naught but their rifles to carry, and could march two miles to our one. But late that afternoon, with Deer's Ears close at hand at last, we sank down along the banks of Owl Creek, the Heecha Wakpa of the Sioux ; built huge fires, scorched our ragged garments, gnawed at tough horse meat, and wondered whether we really ever had tasted such luxuries as ham and eggs or porter - house steak. All night we lay there in the rain ; and at dawn Upham's battalion, with such horses as were thought capable of carrying a rider, were sent off down stream to the southeast on the trail of some wandering Indians who had crossed our front. The rest of us rolled our blankets and trudged out southward. It was Tuesday, the 12th of September, 1876 — a day long to be remembered in the annals of the officers and men of the Big Horn and Yellowstone expedition ; a day that can never be thoroughly described, even could it bear de-

scription ; a day when scores of our horses dropped
exhausted on the trail—when starving men toiled piteously along through thick clinging mud, or flung
themselves, weeping and worn out, upon the broad,
flooded prairie. Happily, we got out of the Bad
Lands before noon ; but one and all were weak with
hunger, and as we dragged through boggy stream-bed,
men would sink hopelessly in the mire and never try to
rise of themselves ; *travois* mules would plunge frantically in bog and quicksand, and pitch the wounded
screaming from their litters. I hate to recall it. Duties kept me with the rear-guard, picking up and driving in stragglers. It was seven A.M. when we marched
from Owl Creek. It was after midnight when Kellogg's rearmost files reached the bivouac along the
Crow. The night was pitchy dark, the rain was pitiless ; half our horses were gone, many of the men
were scattered over the cheerless prairie far behind.
But relief was at hand ; the Belle Fourche was only
a few miles away ; beyond it lay the Black Hills and
the stores of Crook City and Deadwood. Commissary and couriers had been sent ahead to hurry back
provisions ; by noon of the coming sun there would
be abundance.

The morning came slowly enough. All night it
had rained in torrents ; no gleam of sunlight came to
gladden our eyes or thaw the stiffened limbs of our
soldiers. Crow Creek was running like a mill-race.
A third of the command had managed to cross it the
evening before, but the rest had halted upon the northern bank. Roll-call showed that many men had still

failed to catch up, and an examination of the ford revealed the fact that, with precipitous banks above and
below, and deep water rushing over quicksands and
treacherous bottom at the one available point, it must
be patched up in some manner before a crossing could
be effected. An orderly summoned me to the general's headquarters, and there I found him as deep in
the mud as the rest of us. He simply wanted me to
go down and put that ford into shape. "You will
find Lieutenant Young there," said he, "and fifty men
will report to you for duty." Lieutenant Young was
there sure enough, and some fifty men did report, but
there were no tools and the men were jaded; not more
than ten or twelve could do a stroke of work. We
hewed down willows and saplings with our hunting
knives, brought huge bundles of these to the ford,
waded in to the waist, and anchored them as best we
could to the yielding bottom; worked like beavers
until noon, and at last reported it practicable despite
its looks. General Crook and his staff mounted and
rode to the brink, but appearances were against us,
and he plunged in to find a crossing for himself. Vigorous spurring carried him through, though twice we
thought him down. But his horse scrambled up the
opposite bank, the staff followed, dripping, and the
next horseman of the escort went under, horse and
all, and came sputtering to the surface at our shaky
causeway, reached it in safety and floundered ashore.
Then all stuck to our ford—the long column of cavalry, the wounded on their *travois* and the stragglers
—and by two P.M. all were safely over. The Belle

Fourche was only five miles away, but it took two good hours to reach it. The stream was broad, rapid, turbid, but the bottom solid as rock. Men clung to horses' tails or the stirrups of their mounted comrades, and were towed through, and then saddles were whipped off in a dense grove of timber, fires glowed in every direction, herd guards drove the weary horses to rich pastures among the slopes and hillsides south of the creek bottom, and all unoccupied men swarmed out upon the nearest ridge to watch for the coming wagons. Such a shout as went up when the cry was heard, "Rations coming." Such a mob as gathered when the foremost wagon drove in among the famished men. Guards were quickly stationed, but before that could be done the boxes were fairly snatched from their owner and their contents scattered through the surging crowd. Discipline for a moment was forgotten, men fought like tigers for crackers and plugs of tobacco. Officers ran to the scene and soon restored order, but I know that three ginger-snaps I picked up from the mud under the horses' feet and shared with Colonel Mason and Captain Woodson—the first bite of bread we had tasted in three days—were the sweetest morsels we had tasted in years.

By five P.M. wagon after wagon had driven in. Deadwood and Crook City had rallied to the occasion. All they heard was that Crook's army had reached the Belle Fourche, starving. Our commissary, Captain Bubb, had bought, at owners' prices, all the bacon, flour, and coffee to be had. Local dealers had loaded up with every eatable item in their establishments.

Company commanders secured everything the men could need. Then prominent citizens came driving out with welcoming hands and appreciated luxuries, and just as the sun went down Colonel Mason and I were emptying tin cups of steaming coffee and for two mortal hours eating flap-jacks as fast as the cook could turn them out. Then came the blessed pipe of peace, warm, dry blankets, and the soundest sleep that ever tired soldier enjoyed. Our troubles were forgotten.

CHAPTER XIV.

THE BLACK HILLS.

IT was on Wednesday evening that our good friends, the pioneers of Deadwood and Crook City, reached us with their wagons, plethoric with all manner of provender, and the next day, as though in congratulation, the bright sunshine streamed in upon us, and so did rations. The only hard-worked men were the cooks, and from before dawn to late at evening not an hour's respite did they enjoy. Towards sundown we caught sight of Upham's battalion, coming in from its weary scout down stream. They had not seen an Indian, yet one poor fellow, Milner of Comany "A," riding half a mile ahead of them in eager pursuit of an antelope, was found ten minutes after, stripped, scalped, and frightfully gashed and mutilated with knives, stone dead, of course, though still warm. Pony tracks were fresh in the springy sod all around him, but ponies and riders had vanished. Pursuit was impossible. Upham had not a horse that could more than stagger a few yards at a time. The maddest man about it was our Sergeant-Major, Humme, an admirable shot and a man of superhuman nerve and courage ; yet only a few months ago you read how he, with Lieutenant Weir, met a similar fate at the hands of the Utes. He fought a half-score of them single-handed, and sent one of them to his final account before he himself succumbed to the missiles they poured upon him from their shelter in the rocks. A better soldier never lived, and there was grim humor in the statement of the eleven surviving Ute warriors, that they didn't want to fight Weir and Humme, but were obliged to kill them in self-defence. Weir was shot dead before he really saw the adversary, and those twelve unfortunate warriors, armed with their repeaters, would undoubtedly have suffered severely at the hands of Humme and his single shooter if they hadn't killed him too.

This is digressing, but it is so exquisitely characteristic of the Indian Bureau's way of doing things that, now that the peace commissioners have triumphantly announced that the attack on Thornburg's command was all an accident, and have allowed the Indians to bully, temporize, and hoodwink them into weeks of fruitless delay (the rascals never meant to surrender the Meeker murderers so long as they had only peace commissioners to deal with), and now that, after all, the army has probably got to do over again what it started to do last October, and could readily have accomplished long ere this had they not been

hauled off by the Bureau, the question naturally sug-
gests itself, how often is this sort of thing to be repeated? Year after year it has been done. A small
force of soldiers sent to punish a large band of Indian
murderers or marauders. The small band has been
well-nigh annihilated in many instances. Then the
country wakes up, a large force concentrates at vast
expense, and the day of retribution has come, when,
sure as shooting, the Bureau has stepped in with re-
straining hand. No end of silk-hatted functionaries
have hurried out from Washington, shaken hands and
smoked a pipe with a score of big Indians; there has
been a vast amount of cheap oratory and buncombe
talk about the Great Father and guileless red men, at
the end of which we are told to go back to camp and
bury our dead, and our late antagonists, laughing in
their sleeves, link arms with their aldermanic friends,
are "dead-headed" off to Washington, where they
are lionized at the White House, and sent the rounds
of the great cities, and finally return to their reservations laden down with new and improved rifles and
ammunition, stove-pipe hats, and Saratoga trunks,
more than ever convinced that the one way to get
what they want out of Uncle Sam is to slap his face
every spring and shake hands in the fall. The apparent theory of the Bureau is that the soldier is made
to be killed, the Indian to be coddled.

However, deeply as my comrades and myself may
feel on this subject, it does not properly enter into a
narrative article. Let us get back to Upham's battalion, who reached us late on the afternoon of the

fourteenth, desperately tired and hungry. We lost no time in ministering to their wants, though we still had no grain for our horses, but the men made merry over abundant coffee, bacon and beans, and bread and molasses, and were unspeakably happy.

That evening the general decided to send back to the crossings of the swollen streams that had impeded our march on the 12th, and in which many horses and mules and boxes of rifle ammunition had been lost. Indians prowling along our trail would come upon that ammunition as the stream subsided, and reap a rich harvest.

The detail fell upon the Fifth Cavalry. One officer and thirty men to take the back track, dig up the boxes thirty miles away, and bring them in. With every prospect of meeting hundreds of the Sioux following our trail for abandoned horses, the duty promised to be trying and perilous, and when the colonel received the orders from headquarters, and, turning to me, said, " Detail a lieutenant," I looked at the roster with no little interest. Of ten companies of the Fifth Cavalry present, each was commanded by its captain, but subalterns were scarce, and with us such duties were assigned in turn, and the officer "longest in" from scout or detachment service was Lieutenant Keyes. So that young gentleman, being hunted up and notified of his selection, girded up his loins and was about ready to start alone on his perilous trip, when there came swinging up to me an officer of infantry—an old West Point comrade who had obtained permission to make the campaign with the Fifth Cav-

10

alry and had been assigned to Company "I" for duty,
but who was not detailable, strictly speaking, for such
service as Keyes's, from our roster. "Look here, King,
you haven't given me half a chance this last month,
and if I'm not to have this detail, I want to go with
Keyes, as subordinate, or anything ; I don't care, only
I want to go." The result was that he did go, and
when a few days since we read in the *Sentinel* that
Satterlee Plummer, a native of Wisconsin and a grad-
uate of West Point, had been reinstated in the army
on the special recommendation of General Crook, for
gallantry in Indian campaign, I remembered this instance of the Sioux war of 1876, and, looking back to
my note-book, there I found the record and result of
their experience on the back track—they brought in
fourteen horses and all the ammunition without losing
a man.

Now our whole attention was given to the recuperation of our horses—the cavalryman's first thought.
Each day we moved camp a few miles up the lovely
Whitewood valley, seeking fresh grass for the animals, and on September 18th we marched through the
little hamlet of Crook City, and bivouacked again in
a beautiful amphitheatre of the hills, called Centennial Park. From here, dozens of the officers and men
wandered off to visit the mining gulches and settlements in the neighborhood, and numbers were taken
prisoners by the denizens of Deadwood and royally
entertained. General Crook and his staff, with a small
escort, had left us early on the morning of the
16th, to push ahead to Fort Laramie and set about

DEADWOOD CITY, BLACK HILLS OF DAKOTA.

the organization of a force for immediate resumption of business. This threw General Merritt in command of the expedition, and meant that our horses should become the objects of the utmost thought and care. Leaving Centennial Park on the 19th, we marched southward through the Hills, and that afternoon came upon a pretty stream named, as many another is throughout the Northwest, the Box Elder, and there we met a train of wagons, guarded by spruce artillerymen fresh from their casemates on the seaboard, who looked upon our rags with undisguised astonishment, not unmixed with suspicion. But they were eagerly greeted, and that night, for the first time in four long weeks, small measures of oats and corn were dealt out to our emaciated animals. It was touching to see how carefully and tenderly the rough-looking men spread the precious morsels before their steeds, petting them the while, and talking as fond nonsense to their faithful friends as ever mother crooned to sleeping child. It was only a bite for the poor creatures, and their eyes begged wistfully for more. We gave them two nights' rest, and then, having consumed all the grass to be had, pushed on to Rapid Creek, thence again to the southern limits of the Hills, passing through many a mining camp or little town with a name suggestive of the wealth and population of London. We found Custer City a deserted village—many a store and dozens of houses utterly untenanted. No forage to be had for love or money. Our horses could go no farther, so for weeks we lay along French Creek, moving camp every day or two a mile or more for fresh grass. It was dull work, but the men enjoyed it; they were revelling in plenty to eat and no drills, and every evening would gather in crowds around the camp-fires, listening to some favorite vocalist or yarn-spinner. Once in a while letters began to reach us from anxious ones at home, and make us long to see them; and yet no orders came, no definite prospects of relief from our exile. At last, the second week in October started us out on a welcome raid down the valley of the South Cheyenne, but not an Indian was caught napping, and finally, on the 23d of October, we were all concentrated in the vicinity of the Red Cloud Agency to take part in the closing scene of the campaign and assist in the disarming and unhorsing of all the reservation Indians.

General MacKenzie, with the Fourth Cavalry and a strong force of artillery and infantry, was already there, and as we marched southward to surround the Indian camps and villages from the direction of Hat Creek our array was not unimposing, numerically. The infantry, with the "weak-horsed" cavalry, moved along the prairie road. Colonel Royall's command (Third Cavalry and Noyes's Battalion of the Second) was away over to the eastward, and well advanced, so as to envelope the doomed villages from that direction. We of the Fifth spread out over the rolling plain to the west, and in this order all moved towards Red Cloud, twenty odd miles away. It was prettily planned, but scores of wary, savage eyes had watched all Crook's preparations at the agency. The wily Indian was quick to divine that his arms and ponies were threatened, and by noon we had the dismal news by courier that they had stampeded in vast numbers. We enjoyed the further satisfaction of sighting with our glasses the distant clouds of dust kicked up by their scurrying ponies. A few hundred warriors, old men and "blanket Indians," surrendered to MacKenzie, but we of the Big-Horn were empty-handed when once more we met our brigadier upon the following day.

CHAPTER XV.

DROPPED STITCHES.

Now that an unlooked-for interest has been developed in this enterprise of the Sunday *Sentinel,* and that in accordance with the wishes of many old comrades these sketches are reproduced in a little volume by themselves, many and many an incident is recalled which deserves to be noted, but which was omitted for fear of wearying the readers for whom alone these stories of campaign life were originally intended, so that in this closing and retrospective chapter there will be nothing of lively interest, except to those already interested, and it can be dropped right here.

Looking back over it all, more especially the toilsome march and drenching bivouacs that followed the departure from Heart River, I wonder how some men stood it as they did. Among our own officers in the Fifth, one of our best and cheeriest comrades was Lieutenant Bache, "a fellow of infinite jest," and one to whom many of us were greatly attached. He was a martyr to acute rheumatism when he overtook us with Captains Price and Payne, at the headquarters of the Mini Pusa. By the time we met General Terry on the Rosebud, he was in such agonizing helplessness as to be unable to ride a horse, and was ordered to the Yellowstone and thence to Chicago for medical treatment ; but while we lay at the mouth of the Powder River he suddenly reappeared in our midst, and, greatly benefited by the two weeks of rest and dry clothes on the boat, he insisted that he was well enough to resume duty. The surgeons shook their heads, but Bache carried his point with General Crook, and was ordered to rejoin the regiment. Then came day after day of pitiless, pouring rain, night after night unsheltered on the sodden ground. A cast-iron constitution would have suffered ; poor Bache broke down, and, unable to move hand or foot, was lifted into a *travois* and dragged along. When we reached the Black Hills he was reduced to mere skin and bone, hardly a vestige of him left beyond the inexhaustible fund of grit and humor with which he was gifted. He reached Fort Dodge at the close of the campaign, but it had been too much for him. The news of his death was telegraphed by Captain Payne before we had fairly unsaddled for the winter.

Though brother officers in the same regiment, so are our companies scattered at times that before this campaign Bache and I had met but once, and that was in Arizona. To-day the most vivid picture I have in my mind of that trying march in which he figures is a duck-hunting scene that I venture to say has never been equalled in the experience of Eastern sportsmen. We had halted on the evening of September 7th, on the dripping banks of one of the forks of the Grand River (Palanata Wakpa, the Sioux call it, and a much better name it is), a muddy stream, not half the width of our Menominee, but encased between precipitous banks, and swirling in deep, dark pools. The grass was abundant, but not a stick of timber could we find with which to build a fire. While I was hunting for a few crumbs of hard-tack in my lean haversack, there came a sudden sputter of pistol shots on the banks of the stream, and I saw scores of men running, revolver in hand, to the scene. Joining them, I found Bache reclining in his *travois* and blazing away at some objects in the pool below him. The surface of the water was alive with blue-and-green-wing teal, and a regiment of ravenous men was opening fire upon them with calibre-45 bullets. Only fancy it! The wary, gamy bird we steal upon with such caution in our marshes at home, here on the distant prairies, far from the busy haunts of men, so utterly untutored by previous danger, or so utterly bewildered by the fusillade, that hardly one took refuge in flight, while dozens of them, paddling, ducking, diving about the stream, fell victims to the heavy revolver, and, sprinkled with gunpowder for salt, were devoured almost raw by the eager soldiery. "Great Cæsar's ghost," said Bache, as he crammed fresh cartridges into the chambers of his Colt, "what would they say to this on the Chesapeake?"

Another scene with Bache was at Slim Buttes. In order to prevent indiscriminate pillage among the captured lodges of the Sioux, General Crook had ordered the detail of guards to keep out the crowd of curiosity-seekers. Bache was lying very stiff and sore near one of the large tepees, and I had stopped to have a moment's chat with him, when something came crawling out of a hole slashed in the side by the occupants to facilitate their escape when Lieutenant Schwatka charged the village that morning; something so unmistakably Indian that in a second I had brought my revolver from its holster and to full cock. But the figure straightened up in the dim twilight, and with calm deliberation these words fell from its lips: "There ain't a thing worth having in the whole d—d outfit."

Bache burst into amused laughter. "Well, my aboriginal friend, who in thunder are you, anyhow? Your English is a credit to civilization."

It was "Ute John," one of the scouts who had joined us with the Shoshones on the Big Horn, but who, unlike them, had concluded to stand by us through the entire expedition. He was a tall, stalwart fellow, picturesquely attired in an overcoat not unlike our present unsightly ulster in shape, but made of a blanket which had been woven in imitation of numerous rainbows. The storied coat of many colors worn by the original Joseph was never more brilliant than this uncouth garment, and about this time an effort was made to rechristen our sturdy ally, and call him no longer monosyllabic and commonplace John, but Scriptural Joseph. Subsequent developments in his career, however, brought about a revulsion of feeling, as it was found that the fancied resemblance in characteristics ended with the coat.

We had been accustomed in our dealings with the Indians who accompanied us to resort to pantomime as a means of conversation.   Some of our number prided themselves on their mute fluency—none more so, perhaps, than our genial friend Major Andy Burt, of the 9th Infantry, who would "button-hole," so to speak, any Indian who happened along during his unoccupied moments, and the two would soon be lost in a series of gyrations and finger flippings that was a dark mystery to the rest of the command ; and when the major would turn triumphantly towards us with his " He says it's all serene, fellows," we accepted the information as gospel truth without asking what "it" was.   Bache and I were not a little astonished, therefore, at hearing Ute John launch forth into fluent English, albeit strongly tinged with Plains vernacular.

The most tireless men in pursuit of Indian knowledge were the correspondents of the papers.   Frequent mention has already been made of Mr. Finerty, of the *Chicago Times*, who was the gem of the lot, but the *New York Times* and *Herald* were represented, as were leading journals of other large cities.   With one exception they proved excellent campaigners, and welcome, indeed, genial associates ; but the exception was probably one of the most unhappy wretches on the face of the globe.   He had come out as a novice the year previous, and accompanied Colonel Dodge's exploring expedition to the Black Hills, and before long

developed traits of character that made him somewhat
of a nuisance.   He was wofully green, a desperate
coward, but so zealous in the cause of journalism that
anything he fancied might interest the readers of the
paper of which he announced himself "commissioner"
was sent on irrespective of facts in the case.   The
officers found him taking notes of their conversations,
jotting down everything he saw and heard around
camp, caught him prying into matters that were in
nature confidential, and so one night they terrified him
to the verge of dissolution by preparations for defence
and the announcement that the cooing and wooing of
an army of wood-doves were the death-chants of hundreds of squaws as the warriors were stripping for the
combat.   Another time they primed him into writing
a four-column despatch descriptive of the "Camelquo,"
a wonderful animal found only in the Black Hills, the
offspring of the Rocky Mountain elk and the Egyptian
camel, the latter being some of the animals introduced
into Texas just before the war for transportation pur-
poses, who had, so Mr. D—— overheard, escaped from
the rebels and made their way to the Northern plains
during the great rebellion, and there had intermarried
with the great elk, the native of the Hills.   The result-
ant "Camelquo," so D—— enthusiastically informed
his paper, was an animal of the stature of the giraffe,
the antlers of the elk, the humps of the camel, the
fleetness and endurance of both parents, and the unconquerable ferocity of the tiger.   How D—— came to
discover the sell in time, my informant, Dr. McGillicuddy, did not remember, but to this day the maps

of the Black Hills bear commemoration of the incident,
and Camelquo Creek is almost as well known as Spring
and Rapid.   Many a rough miner has asked since '75
how in Hades, or words to that effect, they came to
have such queer names for their streams in the Hills.
Most of them were named by Colonel Dodge's party,
and there was rhyme or reason in each, even for Amphibious Creek, which, said McGillicuddy, we so named
because it sank out of sight so often and came up smiling so unexpectedly that it only seemed half land, half
water.

On the campaign of '76, Mr. D—— again made
his appearance as commissioner, started with General
Crook's staff, but ere long was called upon to find new
accommodations elsewhere.   How it all came about I
never cared to know, but after unpleasant experiences
with first one set and then another, he gravitated
eventually to the packers, who made him do guard and
herd duty.   He pushed ahead with Major Mills's command, and stumbled with them into the morning battle
at Slim Buttes.   This he witnessed in a state of abject
terror, and then, when the danger was over, wrote a
most scandalous account, accusing Major Mills of all
manner of misbehavior.   His paper published it, but
had to eat humble pie, make a most complete apology,
and, I think, dismiss its correspondent.   Camelquo
Creek is the only existing trace of poor D—— of which
we have any knowledge.

Once fairly in the Black Hills, and resting on the
banks of French Creek, we set to work to count up the
losses of the campaign.   In horseflesh and equipments

the gaps were appalling. Some companies in the Fifth were very much reduced, and, of course, when the horse dropped exhausted on the trail, there was no transportation for the saddle, bridle, and "kit." It often happened that for days the soldier led his horse along the flanks of the column or in the rear of the regiment, striving hard to nurse his failing strength, hunting eagerly for every little bunch of grass that might eke out his meagre subsistence. In all the array of company losses there was one, and only one, shining contrast—Montgomery, with Company "B," the Grays, calmly submitted a clear "bill of health;" he had not lost a single horse, which was marvellous in itself, but when "Monty" proceeded to state that every Company "B" man had his saddle, bridle, nose bag, lariat, picket-pin, side lines, etc., the thing was incomprehensible; that is, it seemed incomprehensible, until the fact was taken into consideration that those companies which bivouacked on either flank of the Grays woke each morning to the realization of a predatory ability on the part of "them d—d Company 'B' fellers" that rose superior to any defensive devices they might invent. But Company "B" could not acquire gray horses at the expense of the rest of the regiment, whatever it might have done in side and other lines, and the fact that Captain "Monty" paraded every horse with which he started is due to the unerring judgment and ceaseless vigilance with which he noted every symptom of weakness in any and every animal in his troop, and cared for it accordingly.

As a rule, our company commanders are not thorough

horsemen, and too little attention is devoted to the in-
struction of our cavalry officers in the subject—but
Montgomery is a noteworthy exception. I don't know
which class will be the more inclined to think me in
error in the following statement, but as a result of not
a little observation it is my opinion that, while the
best riders in the cavalry service come from West
Point, the best horsemen are from the ranks.

But for our anxiety about our horses, the most enjoyable days of the campaign were probably contained
in the first two weeks of October. We were the rough-
est-looking set of men on the face of the globe ; but
with abundant rations and rousing big fires along the
valley of French Creek, with glad letters from home,
and finally the arrival of our wagons with the forgotten luxuries of tents and buffalo robes, we began
taking a new interest in life. The weather was superb, the sun brilliant, the air keen and bracing, the
nights frostily cold. Wonderful appetites we had in
those days, and after supper the men would gather in
crowds around the camp-fires and sing their songs and
smoke their pipes in placid contentment. The officers,
too, had their reunions, though vocalists were scarce
among them, and the proportions of " youngsters " who
keep the fun alive was far too small. The year before,
those irrepressible humorists, Harrigan and Hart, of the
New York stage, had sung at their " Théâtre Comique "
a witty but by no means flattering ditty, which they
called " The Regular Army, O." One of its verses,
slightly modified to suit the hearers, was particularly
applicable to and popular in the Fifth Cavalry, and

their adjutant, when he could be made to sing "*pro bono publico*," was always called upon for the song and sure of applause at the close of this verse.   It ran:

" We were sent to Arizona, for to fight the Indians there;
  We were almost snatched bald-headed, but they didn't get
       our hair.
  We lay among the cañons and the dirty yellow mud,
  But we seldom saw an onion, or a turnip, or a spud,
  Till we were taken prisoners and brought forninst the chief;
  Says he, " We'll have an Irish stew "—the dirty Indian thief.
  On Price's telegraphic wire we slid to Mexico,
  And we blessed the day we skipped away from the Regular
       Army, O."

Now General Crook received his promotion to briga- dier-generalship in Arizona, after a stirring and vic- torious campaign with the Apaches, and the Fifth Cavalry used to boast at times that his " star" was won for him by them.   Soldiers are quick to attach some expressive nickname to their officers, but I never learned that our general had won this questionable distinction until we joined him at Goose Creek, when we found that in the command already there he was know as " Rosebud George."

In the hard times that followed there was no little growling among the half-starving troopers, because the packers seemed to have sufficient to eat when we were well-nigh destitute.   So one night a fifth verse was trolled out on the still evening air in a strongly Hibernian brogue, and the listening ears of the Fifth were greeted with something like this:

"But 'twas out upon the Yellowstone we had the d—dest time,
  Faix, we made the trip wid Rosebud George, six months
       without a dime.

"THE DANDY FIFTH."

(General Merritt and his Officers on the Sioux Campaign.)

Some eighteen hundred miles we went through hunger, mud,
 and rain,
Wid backs all bare, and rations rare, no chance for grass or
 grain ;
Wid 'bunkies shtarvin' by our side, no rations was the rule ;
Shure 'twas ate your boots and saddles, you brutes, but feed
 the packer and mule.
But you know full well that in your fights no soldier lad was
 slow,
And it wasn't the packer that won ye a star in the Regular
 Army, O."

With full stomachs, however, came forgetfulness
of suffering, and this with other campaign lyrics was
forgotten.

It seemed so good to rest in peace for day after day.
General Merritt with his staff, and Major Upham, had
pitched their tents in the shelter of a little rocky prom-
ontory that jutted out into the valley and was crowned
by a sparse growth of pines and cedars.   One evening, as the full moon shone down upon the assembled
party over this ridge, a perfectly defined cross appeared upon the very face of the luminary.   Every
one noticed it, and one of the number, clambering to
the summit, found growing from a cleft in the rock a
sturdy little leafless branch about two feet in length,
crossed by another and smaller twig; the cross was
perfect, and the effect in the moonlight something
simply exquisite.   " Camp Faith " was thereupon se-
lected as the name of cavalry headquarters.   Somebody wanted a name for the Fifth Cavalry camp, and,
in recognition of our present blissful and undisturbed
existence, as compared with recent vicissitudes, and

mindful of the martial palace of Sans Souci at Potsdam, a wildly imprudent subaltern suggested *Sans Sioux Ici*, but it was greeted with merited contempt.

Of course all were eager for intimation of our next move. Occasional despatches reached General Merritt, but not a hint could be extracted from him. Rumors of a winter campaign were distressingly prevalent, and the Fifth were beginning to look upon a prolonged stay in the Hills as a certainty, when one day an aide-de-camp of the chief's came to me with the request that I would make a map for him of the country between the South Cheyenne and Red Cloud Agency, and let no one know what I was doing. A week after he wanted another sketch of the same thing, and it became evident, to me at least, that before very long we would be down along the White River, looking after "Machpealota."

The campaign itself being virtually over, the recruits authorized by special act of Congress to be enlisted for the cavalry regiments actively engaged began to be heard of at the front, and one evening in early October we learned that some four hundred heroes were on the march from Fort Laramie to join the Fifth, and that the Third was to be similarly reinforced. A hint as to the probable character of the new levies was also in circulation. Twenty-five hundred men having been suddenly and urgently needed, the recruiting officers were less particular in their selections than would otherwise have been the case, and from the purlieus of Philadelphia, Baltimore, and New York the scum of the country was eagerly grasping this method of getting to the Black Hills at Uncle Sam's expense. They were marching up to join us, under the command of Captain Monahan, of the Third Cavalry, assisted by Lieutenants Ward, Cherry, and Swift, "of Ours;" and on the 11th of October General Merritt struck camp, the "B., H., and Y.," horse, foot, and dragoon, bade farewell to French Creek, and, after an exhilarating ride through a wildly beautiful and picturesque tract of the Hills, we unsaddled, pitched our tents along Amphibious Creek, and that evening the new levies arrived. Nobody cared particularly to see the recruits, but the Fifth Cavalry turned out to a man to see the new horses; and having called upon and extended a welcoming hand to the comrades joining us for the first time, we made a dash for the quadrupeds. Before tattoo that evening there was not one that had not been closely inspected and squabbled over by the company commanders and their men, and the first thing the next morning General Merritt ordered the distribution of horses, " according to color," to companies.

It was revealed that an expedition somewhere was intended by his directing the regimental adjutant to pick out the old soldiers among the recruits, assign them to companies at once, and then issue orders to the regiment to be in readiness to move at daybreak.

Never in my life have I seen such an array of vagabonds as that battalion of four hundred " unassigned " when I got them into line on the morning of the 12th of October and proceeded to "pick out the old soldiers " as directed. That was a matter of no difficulty; they were already acting as non-commissioned officers of

11

the recruit companies, but were not sixty all told, and more were needed. Stopping before a sturdily built little fellow with a grizzled moustache and an unmistakably soldierly carriage, the only promising-looking man left in the three hundred who had "stood fast" when the order was given "men who have served previous enlistments step to front," the adjutant questioned:

"Haven't you served before?"

"Not in the regulars, sir."

"That man is lame, sir," interposed a sergeant.

"It is an old wound," says the man eagerly, "and it's only so once in while. I can ride first-rate."

"What was your regiment?"

"Seventh Wisconsin, sir."

"What! Were you at Gainesville?"

"Yes, sir. Wounded there."

A knot of officers—Merritt, Mason, Sumner, and Montgomery—who fought through the war with the Army of the Potomac, are standing there as the adjutant turns.

"Sergeant, take this man to Company "K" and fit him out—and—stop a moment. Bring him to my tent to-night after supper. Gentlemen, that's an Iron Brigade man."

That evening a Company "K" sergeant scratches the flap of the adjutant's tent—you cannot knock when there is no door—and presents himself with the recruit-veteran. The latter looks puzzled, but perfectly self-possessed; answers without hesitation two or three rapidly propounded questions as to names of his regimental officers in '62, and then seems completely bewildered as the adjutant takes him cordially by the hand and bids him welcome. However, it did not require many words to explain the matter.

To return to those recruits. If the police force of our large Eastern cities were at a loss to account for the disappearance of a thousand or more of their "regular boarders," a flying trip to the Black Hills on this 12th day of October, '76, would have satisfied them as to their whereabouts. Where there were ten "good men and true" among the new-comers, there were forty who came simply with the intention of deserting when they got fairly into the Hills and within striking distance of the mines, an intention most successfully carried out by a large proportion of their number.

And then the names under which they enlisted! "What's your name?" said the adjutant to the most unmistakable case of "Bowery Boy" in the front rank.

"My name's Jackson Bewregard," is the reply, with the accompaniment of hunching shoulders, projecting chin, overlapping under-lip, and sneering nostril characteristic of Chatham Square in the palmy days of Mose.

"And yours?" to Mr. Bewregard's left file, a big rough of Hiberniar extraction.

"My name's Jooles Vern."

The adjutant glances at the muster-roll: "'No. 173—Jules Verne.' Ha! yes. The party that wrote 'Around the World in Eighty Days.' Have we many more of these eminent Frenchmen, sergeant?"

The sergeant grins under his great moustache. Possibly he is recalling a fact which the adjutant has by no means forgotten, that ten years before, when they were both in General Billy Graham's famous light battery of the First Artillery, of which the adjutant was then second lieutenant, the sergeant was then, too, a sergeant, but with a very different name.

Friday, October 13th—ill-omened day of the week, ill-omened day of the month—and we were to start on a scout down into the valley of the Cheyenne. Perhaps three fourths of our number neither knew nor cared what day it was; but, be that as it may, there was an utterly unmistakable air of gloom about our move. The morning was raw and dismal. "The General" sounded soon after nine, and the stirring notes fell upon seemingly listless ears; no one seemed disposed to shout, whistle, or sing, and just at ten o'clock, when we were all standing to horse and ready to start, Major Sumner's company sent forth a mournful little procession towards the new-made grave we had marked on the hillside at the sharp bend of the creek, and with brief service, but sad enough hearts, the body of a comrade who had died the night before was lowered to its rest. The carbines rang out the parting volleys, and Bradley's trumpet keened a wailing farewell. General Merritt and his staff, coming suddenly upon us during the rites, silently dismounted and uncovered until the clods rattled in upon the soldier's rude coffin, and all was over. Then, signalling us to follow, the chief rode on, the Fifth swung into saddle, and with perceptibly augmented ranks followed in his tracks. A battalion of the Third Cavalry, under Colonel Van Vliet, and a detachment of the Second, under Captain Peale, accompanied us, while the infantry bat-

talion, the rest of the cavalry, the recruits, and the
sick or disabled remained in camp under command of
Colonel Royall.   Where were we going?   What was
expected?   None knew behind the silent horseman at
the head of column ; but a start on Friday, the 13th,
to the mournful music of a funeral march, boded ill
for success.   However, not to be harrowing, it is as
well to state right here that ten days from that date
the scout was over, and, without having lost man or
horse, the Fifth rode serenely into Red Cloud Agency.
So far as the regiment was concerned that supersti-
tion was exploded.

The march down Amphibious Creek was grandly
beautiful as to scenery.   We wound, snake-like, along
the stream, gliding under towering, pine - covered
heights, or bold, rocky precipices.   The valley opened
out wider as we neared the " sinks," and, finally, turning abruptly to the right, we dismounted and led our
horses over a lofty ridge, bare of trees, and commanding a broad valley to the south, over which the road
stretched in long perspective till lost in dark Buffalo
Gap, the only exit through the precipitous and lofty
range that hemmed in the plain between us and the
Cheyenne valley beyond.   Here we encountered an
emigrant train slowly toiling up the southern slope
and staring at us in undisguised wonderment.   Ten
miles away we came once again "plump" upon the boil-
ing waters of the creek, where it reappeared after a
twelve-mile digression in the bowels of the earth.   It
was clear and fair when it left us in the valley behind
to take its plunge, and it met us again with a more than
troubled appearance and the worst kind of an odor.

Square in between the massive portals of the great gap we unsaddled at sunset and encamped for the night.

In the scout which ensued down the valley of the South Cheyenne there was absolutely nothing of sufficient interest to record in these pages. Nor had we any luck in our participation in the "round-up" at the Indian reservation on the 22d and 23d of October. Such warriors as had remained near Camp Robinson meekly surrendered to General MacKenzie, and we had nothing to do but pitch our tents side by side with the new-comers of the Fourth Cavalry and wonder what was to come next. General Crook was known to be in the garrison with his aides-de-camp, and we had not long to wait. On the 24th of October our motley array received the welcome order to go into winter-quarters, the Fifth Cavalry on the line of the Union Pacific Railroad, and within another twenty-four hours we were *en route* for the comforts of civilization.

But, before we separated from the comrades with whom we had marched and growled these many weary miles, our chief gave us his parting benediction in the following words:

"HEADQUARTERS BIG HORN AND YELLOWSTONE EXPEDITION,
                CAMP ROBINSON, NEB., *October* 24, 1876.
"*General Orders No.* 8.

"The time having arrived when the troops composing the Big Horn and Yellowstone Expedition are about to separate, the brigadier-general commanding addresses himself to the officers and men of the command to say :

"In the campaign now closed he has been obliged to call upon you for much hard service and many sacrifices of personal comfort. At times you have been out of reach of your base of supplies ; in most inclement weather you have marched without food and slept without shelter ; in your engagements you have evinced a high order of discipline and courage ; in your marches, wonderful powers of endurance ; and in your deprivations and hardships, patience and fortitude.

"Indian warfare is, of all warfare, the most dangerous, the most trying, and the most thankless. Not recognized by the high authority of the United States Senate as war, it still possesses for you the disadvantages of civilized warfare, with all the horrible accompaniments that barbarians can invent and savages execute. In it you are required to serve without the incentive to promotion or recognition ; in truth, without favor or hope of reward.

"The people of our sparsely settled frontier, in whose defence this war is waged, have but little influence with the powerful communities in the East ; their representatives have little voice in our national councils, while your savage foes are not only the wards of the nation, supported in idleness, but objects of sympathy with large numbers of people otherwise well-informed and discerning.

"You may, therefore, congratulate yourselves that, in the performance of your military duty, you have been on the side of the weak against the strong, and that the few people there are on the frontier will remember your efforts with gratitude.

"If, in the future, it should transpire that the avenues * for recognition of distinguished services and gallant conduct are opened, those rendered in this campaign will be remembered.

* * * * * * * * * * *

" BY COMMAND OF BRIGADIER-GENERAL CROOK.

(*Signed*)   JOHN G. BOURKE,
" *First Lieutenant Third Cavalry,
A.D.C., and A.A.A. General.*"

---

* The avenue was at last opened by the signature of the President to the bill providing that brevet rank might be conferred on officers for gallant conduct in Indian warfare, but it came just too late. General Crook had barely time to express his gratification. He died within the week that followed, and his list of officers recommended for brevets for services rendered in this campaign died with him.

To use the emphatic vernacular of the frontier, that parting order "just filled the bill." It was as complete a summing-up of the disadvantages of Indian campaigning as could well be written; it indicated plainly how thoroughly our general had appreciated the sufferings of his men on that hideous march from Heart River; it assured us of the sympathy he had felt for one and all (though I doubt if ever a one of us suffered half so much as he); and, finally, in tendering the thanks of our commander, it conveyed the only reward we could possibly expect, for had he not truly said that, of all warfare, Indian warfare is the most thankless?

Well, it was over with, so far as we were concerned, though brief was our respite, and now came the closing scenes before the rising of the morning's sun should see us split up into battalions or detachments, and, with light feet and lighter hearts, marching away to the south.

All night long, at General Crook's headquarters, his tireless staff were working away at orders and details of the move, and closing his report to the lieutenant-general at Chicago; and here, too, my services were kept in requisition preparing the map which was to accompany the written report, so that, for us at least, there was no opportunity of sharing in the parting festivities and bidding farewell to comrades, cavalry and infantry, separating for the new posts and the duties of recuperation.

Our farewells were hurried, yet even now, how vividly I recall the faces that crowded round headquar-

ters that bright morning of the 25th.   Bronzed and
bearded, rugged with the glow of health, or pallid
from wounds and illness, but all kindly and cordial.
Then, too, the scenes of our campaign seemed passing
in review before me, and, dream-like, they linger with
me still.   Glancing over these now completed pages,
how utterly meagre and unsatisfactory the record
seems; how many an incident have I failed to mention; how many a deed of bravery or self-denial is left
untold.   I look back through the mists and rain into
the dark depths of that bloody ravine at Slim Buttes,
and wonder how I could ever have told the story of
its assault and failed to speak of how our plucky Milwaukee sergeant sprang down in the very face of the
desperately fighting Indians and picked up a wounded Third Cavalryman and carried him on his back out
of further harm's way; and of brave, noble-hearted
Munson, as true a soldier as ever commanded company, rushing in between two fires to drag the terrified squaws from their peril; of Bache, "swollen,
puffed, and disfigured with rheumatism, conquering
agony to mount his horse and take part in the action;"
of Rodgers, striding down the slopes in front of his
skirmish-line, his glorious voice ringing above the
clamor, laughing like a schoolboy at the well-meant
efforts of the Indian sharpshooters to pick him off; of
General Carr, riding out to the front on his conspicuous gray, and sitting calmly there to show the men
what wretched shots some Indians could be.

How could half the incidents be told when so little
parade was made of them at the time?   Who knew

the night of the stampede on the Rosebud that Eaton was shot through the hand until he had spent an hour or more completing his duties, riding as though nothing had happened? Who knew, at the Rosebud battle, that Nickerson's exertions in the saddle had reopened the old Gettysburg wound and well-nigh finished him? We thought he looked white and wan when he rejoined us at Red Cloud, but never divined the cause. From first to last throughout that march of eight hundred miles, so varied in its scenes, but so utterly changeless in discomfort, there was a spirit of uncomplaining "take-it-as-a-matter-of-course" determination that amounted at times among the men to positive heroism. Individual pluck was thoroughly tested, and the instances of failure were few and far between.

Despite the fact that our engagements were indecisive at the time (and Indian fights that fall short of annihilation on either side generally are), the campaign had its full result. Sitting Bull's thousands were scattered in confusion over the Northwest, he himself driven to a refuge " across the line," his subordinates broken up into dejected bands that, one after another, were beaten or starved into submission, and in the following year General Crook's broad department, the grand ranges of the Black Hills and Big Horn, the boundless prairies of Nebraska and Wyoming, were as clear of hostile warriors as, two years before, they were of settlers, and to-day the lovely valleys of the North, thanks to his efforts, and the ceaseless vigilance of Generals Terry and Miles in guarding the line, are the peaceful homes of hundreds of hardy pioneers.

ROSTER OF OFFICERS

SERVING WITH THE FIFTH CAVALRY IN THE BIG HORN AND YELLOWSTONE EXPEDITION OF 1876.

Colonel WESLEY MERRITT, Brevet Major-General.
Lieutenant-Colonel EUGENE A. CARR, Brevet Major-General.
Major JOHN J. UPHAM.
Major JULIUS W. MASON, Brevet Lieutenant-Colonel.
Captain EDWARD H. LEIB, Brevet Lieutenant-Colonel.
Captain SAMUEL S. SUMNER, Brevet Major.
Captain EMIL ADAM.
Captain ROBERT H. MONTGOMERY.
Captain SANFORD C. KELLOGG, Brevet Lieutenant-Colonel.
Captain GEORGE F. PRICE.
Captain EDWARD M. HAYES.
Captain J. SCOTT PAYNE.
Captain ALBERT E. WOODSON.
Captain CALBRAITH P. RODGERS.
First Lieutenant BERNARD REILLY, Jr.
First Lieutenant WM. C. FORBUSH, A.A.G. Cavalry Brigade.
First Lieutenant CHARLES KING, Adjutant.
First Lieutenant WILLIAM P. HALL, Quartermaster.
First Lieutenant WALTER S. SCHUYLER, A.D.C. to General Crook.
Second Lieutenant CHARLES D. PARKHURST.
Second Lieutenant CHARLES H. WATTS (until July, when disabled).
Second Lieutenant EDWARD W. KEYES.
Second Lieutenant ROBERT LONDON.
Second Lieutenant GEORGE O. EATON (until August 24th, disabled August 10th).
Second Lieutenant HOEL S. BISHOP.
Lieutenant WM. C. HUNTER, U. S. N. ("Brevet Commodore").
Second Lieutenant ROBT. H. YOUNG, 4th Inf., A.D.C. to General Merritt.
Second Lieutenant J. HAYDEN PARDEE, 23d Inf., A.D.C. to General Merritt.
Second Lieutenant SATTERLEE C. PLUMMER, 4th Inf., with Co. "I."
Acting Assistant Surgeon J. W. POWELL.

CAPTAIN SANTA CLAUS.

THERE was unusual commotion in the frontier mining town when the red stage, snow-covered and storm-beaten, lurched up in front of the Bella Union and began to disgorge passengers and mail. The crowd on the wooden sidewalk was of that cosmopolitan type which rich and recently discovered "leads" so surely attract—tough-looking miners ; devil-may-care cow-boys with rolling hat-brims and barbaric display of deadly weapons ; a choice coterie of gamblers with exaggerated suavity of manners ; several impassive Chinamen (very clean) ; several loafing Indians (very dirty) ; a brace of spruce, clean-shaven, trim-built soldiers from the garrison down the valley ; and the inevitable squad of "beats" with bleary eyes and wolfish faces infesting the doorways of the saloons, sublimely trustful of a community that had long ceased to trust them, and scenting eleemosynary possibilities in each new-comer.

But while the arrival of the stage was a source of perennial excitement in the business centre of Argentopolis, the commotion on this occasion was due to the tumultuous welcome given by a mob of school-children to a tall, bronzed, fiercely moustached party the instant he stepped, fur-clad, from the dark interior. Such an

array of eager, joyous little faces one seldom sees.
Big boys and wee maidens, they threw themselves
upon him with shrill clamor and enthusiastic embraces,
swarming about his legs as, with twinkling eyes and
genial greeting, he lifted the little ones high in air
and kissed their dimpled cheeks, and shook the struggling boys heartily by the hand, and was pulled this
way and that way until eventually borne off in triumph
towards the spickspan new shop, with its glittering
white front and alluring display of fruit, pastry, and
confectionery, all heralded forth under the grandilo-
quent but delusive sign, "Bald Eagle Bakery."

Upon this tumultuous reception Argentopolis gazed
for some moments in wondering silence. When the
transfer of the children and their willing captive to a
point some dozen yards away rendered conversation a
possibility, the spokesman of the sidewalk committee
shifted his quid, and formulated in frontier phrase the
question which seemed uppermost in the public mind :

"Who 'n thunder's that ?"

"That ?" said the soldier addressed. "That's Captain Ransom. It's good times the kids 'll be having
now."

"B'long to your rigiment ?"

"Yes ; captain of 'B' troop. Been away on leave
ever since we got here."

"Seems fond o' children," said the Argentopolitan,
reflectively. "Got any of his own ?"

"Nary. He b'longs to the whole crowd. The 'B'
company fellers 'll be glad he's back. They think as
much of him as the kids do."

"Good officer, eh?"

"You bet; ain't no better in the cavalry."

At this unequivocal endorsement from expert authority the eyes of Argentopolis again followed the big man in the fur overcoat. With three or four youngsters tugging at each hand, and a dozen revolving irregularly about him, he was striding across the street, keeping up a running fire of chatter with his throning satellites. Soldier he was unquestionably. Tall, erect of carriage, broad of shoulder, deep of chest, with a keen, quick glance from under his heavy brows. Eyes full of light and fire, nose straight and prominent, a great moustache that hid the curves of his handsome mouth and swept out across the square and resolute jaws—a moustache that, like the wavy brown hair about the temples, was tingeing with gray. Strong white teeth glistened through the drooping thatch, and one or two merry dimples dotted his bronzed and weather-beaten cheeks.

Over on the neighboring side street, from the steps of the schoolhouse, other children surveyed the group, and with envious eyes and watering mouths beheld the demolition of tarts and turnovers. Despite the keen and searching cold of the mountain air, rare and still and brimming with ozone as November days can ever find it, the school shoved its hands deep in trousers pockets and stared with all its youthful might.

Even so blessed a half-hour must have its end, and as the warning bell began to ring, and the Townies to shout that "reecess" was over, the merry throng, spoil-laden, came pouring down the bakery steps, with

12

many admonitions to their big benefactor not to think of starting for the fort until school was out and they could escort him home. Two or three of the smallest still clung to him, explaining that only the big ones had afternoon school; *they* were all through; they had nothing to do until the ambulance came to take them all at four o'clock; and the captain became suddenly aware of two little people standing on the sidewalk and regarding him wistfully. One was a sturdy boy of seven, with frank blue eyes and chubby rounded cheeks—a picture of solid young America despite the fact that his little fists were red and bare; his knickerbockers, though well fitting, were worn and patched; and the copper toes of his cheap, heavy boots were wearing suspiciously thin. He stood protectingly by a little maiden, whose face was like those of Sir Joshua Reynolds's seraphs — a face as pure an oval as ever sculptor modelled or painter limned, with great, lustrous, long-lashed eyes and delicate and dainty features, and all about it tumbled a wealth of glistening golden hair, and all over it shone the look of childish longing and almost piteous entreaty. One little mittened hand was clasped in her brother's; the other, uncovered, hung by a finger in her rosy mouth. She was warmly clad; her little cloak and hood were soft and white and fleecy; her pigmy legs were cased in stout worsted, and her feet in warm "arctics," and "mother's darling" was written in every ornament of her dress.

Ransom, stowing away a handful of silver, came suddenly upon this silent pair, and stopped short.

Another instant and he had stooped, raised the younger child in his strong hands, and with caressing tone accosted her :

"Why, little Snow-drop, who are you? What a little fairy you are !"

"She ain't one of us," piped up a youthful patrician, disdainfully. "She's infantry. He's her brother, and they don't belong to the fort."

The boy's face flushed, and he looked reproachfully at the speaker, but said no word. Ransom was gazing with singular intentness into the downcast face of his little captive.

"Won't you tell me your name, little one?" he pleaded. "Why didn't you come in and have some tarts and turnovers with the others? I've got to run now and meet some other old fellows at the stage office. Here, little man," he said, as he set her down, "take Snow-drop in for me, and you two just eat all you can, and you pay for it for me." He held out a bright half-dollar. Snow-drop's eyes glistened, and she looked eagerly at her brother.

But the boy hung back. For an instant he hesitated, screwing his boot toe into a convenient knot-hole as means of covering his embarrassment. "Come, Jack," said the captain, reassuringly, touching him on the shoulder. The little fellow shook his head.

"Why not, my boy?" pleaded Ransom. "Papa won't mind, when you tell him it was old Uncle Hal. That's what they call me."

A lump rose in the youngster's throat. His head went lower.

"It—it's mamma wouldn't like it," he finally said ; and just then, with rush and sputter of hoofs, two officers came trotting around the corner, threw themselves from their saddles, pounced upon their comrade, and overwhelmed him with joyous greeting. Another minute and others arrived, and between them all he was led away up the street. While some of the children confidently followed, two remained behind—little Snow-drop, refusing to be comforted, was applying the back of her mittened hand to her weeping eyes, and turning a deaf ear to her manful brother, who was vainly striving to explain matters.

"Maudie Carleton's crying because Phil wouldn't take the money and get her some goodies," said little Jack Wilkins, in an opportune pause.

"Who did you say ?" asked Ransom, turning suddenly, and looking inquiringly at his friends. There was an instant of embarrassment. Then one of the officers replied,

"Maud Carleton, Ransom. Those are poor Phil Carleton's little ones."

"Wait for me at the office, fellows ; I'll be along in a minute," was the response ; and the captain went striding back to the Bald Eagle.

It was an old story in the cavalry. Very few there were who knew not that Captain Ransom was a hard-hit man when Kate Perry—the beauty of her father's regiment—came back from school, and with all the wealth of her grace and loveliness and winning ways, refusing to see how she had impressed one or two "solid" men of the garrison, fell rapturously in love

"'COME, JACK,' SAID THE CAPTAIN, REASSURINGLY."

with Philip Carleton, the handsome, dashing scape-grace of the subalterns. It was "hard lines" for old Colonel Perry ; it would have been misery to her de-voted mother ; but she was spared it all—the grass had been growing for years over her distant grave.

The wedding was a glitter of gold-lace, champagne glasses, and tears. Every one wished her—and him—all happiness, but dreaded the future. There was a year of bliss, and little Phil was born ; another year when she was much taken up with her baby boy, and the father much abroad—a year of clouds and silence. Then came sudden call to the field, and one night with reeling senses she read the despatch that told her he was shot dead in battle with the Sioux. When little Maudie came there was no father to receive her in his arms. The gray-haired colonel took the widow and her children a few short years to his own roof ; then he, too, was called to his account, and with a widow's pension and the relic of her father's savings the sor-rowing woman moved from the garrison that had so long been her home, and took up arms against her sea of troubles. She need not have gone. All Fort Rains knew that there were officers who would gladly have taken her and her beautiful children to their fireside. But she was loyal, proud, high-spirited, and she could not stay. All the roof her father had to leave her was the frame cottage at the ranch he had bought and stocked, a mile below the fort. She was a sol-dier's daughter, brave and resolute, she had her fa-ther's old soldier-servant and his wife to help her, and she moved to the ranch, and declared she would be

dependent on no one. When first she had come into
that glorious valley, a girl of eighteen, a large force
of cavalry was encamped around the garrison in which
her father's regiment of foot was stationed, and Captain Harold Ransom became one of her most devoted
admirers, though nearly twice her age. Few men had
much chance against such a lover as Phil Carleton,
buoyant, brilliant, gallant, the pride of all the juniors
in the infantry, the despair of many a prudent mother;
and when that engagement was announced, the cavalry
were rather glad to be ordered away, and to comfort
themselves with the perilous distractions of Indian
fighting for three or four stirring years. But, before
they left, Ransom and others had bought much of the
land on which Argentopolis gleamed to-day. Perhaps
it was the silver that came into his hair as well as his
pockets, but silver did not cause the lines that crept
under his kindly eyes and around the corners of the
firm mouth. He was rich, as army men go, but his
heart was sorely wrenched. He went abroad when
the Indian campaigns were over, and rejoined while
his comrades were on the Pacific coast, and became
the delight of the children and the children's mothers.
Captain Santa Claus they called him at Walla Walla
and Vancouver, where he was the life of those garrisons ; and while men honored and women waxed
sentimental towards him, it was the children who took
possession of the tall soldier and made his house their
home, who trooped unbidden all over it at any hour
of the day, and made it the garrison play-ground when
the rainy season set in and drove them to cover.

And then, after their four years in the Columbia country, the regiment crossed the big range, and, wonder of wonders, headquarters and six troops, one of them Ransom's, were ordered to Fort Rains! He was again on long leave when the change of station occurred, and the widow drew a long breath. She found life very different, with her father's old friends and hers removed. As the children grew in years their needs increased. She sold the stock and much of the land of the Ranch, keeping only the homestead and the patch around it, but she was glad to find employment at the fort as teacher of the piano and singing. She played well, but her voice was glorious, and had been carefully trained. The news that he was coming had given her a shock. It was more than eight years since she had seen him. It was more than five since she had briefly answered the letter he wrote her on hearing of her husband's death. It was so manly, sympathetic, and so full of something he knew not how to express—a longing to shield her from wanv or care. She had gently but firmly ended it all.

And yet— She was bitterly poor now. Handsomer than ever, said the officers who knew her in the old days ; still wearing her mourning, and looking so tall and majestic in her rusting weeds. She was a woman whose form and carriage would be noticeable anywhere—tall, slender, graceful, with a certain slow, languorous ease of motion that charmed the senses. Her face was exquisite in contour and feature—a pure type of blond, blue-eyed, Saxon beauty, with great masses of shimmering golden-brown hair. No wonder Ransom felt a thrill when he looked into Maudie's eyes—the child was her mother in miniature. At twenty-seven, with all her trials, Mrs. Carleton was a lovelier woman than in her maiden radiance at eighteen. What she had gained in strength and character, through her years of poverty and self-abnegation, God alone knew, and He had been her comforter.

For nearly a year the garrison children had been going in to town for school, an excellent teacher having been secured in the East, and Mrs. Carleton eagerly embraced the chance of sending hers. She could no longer afford a nurse to look after the wee one. She could not take her on her daily round of lessons, and her infantry friends had gladly seen to it that the little Carletons were carried to and fro with their own. So, too, when the cavalry came had Colonel Cross assured her that the ambulance should always come for them and bring them back to the post. Everybody wanted to be kind to her, or said so at least; but the ladies were all new and strange. She had never been the pet among them she was in her own regiment. They had not known and loved her father, as had the colonel. They had heard of handsome Phil Carleton, as who had not? but they had heard of Hal Ransom's old-time devotion to her, and now he would soon be back. Rich, growing gray, everybody's friend, the children's idol—oh! what if she should set that widow's cap for him now! The possibility was appalling.

And Christmas was coming, and the children had been weaving glowing pictures of the bliss to be theirs because Captain Santa Claus was homeward bound, and little Maud was listening with eager ears, and her blue-eyed brother in silent longing. The boy was his mother's knight and champion. She took him into her confidence and told him many of her troubles, and time and again after Maudie was asleep the two were rocking in the big arm-chair in front of the hearth, the little fellow curled up in her lap, his arms around her neck, his ruddy cheek nestled against hers, that looked so fragile and white by contrast. He knew how hard a struggle mamma was having in keeping the wolf from the door, and he was helping her—little hero that he was—wearing uncomplainingly the patched knickerbockers and cowhide boots, bearing in soldier silence the thoughtless jeers of his schoolmates, and taking comfort in the fact that sensitive little Maud was always prettily dressed. She had been petted from babyhood, for scarlet-fever had left her weak and nervous.

And so the coming of glad Christmas-tide was not to them the source of boundless joy it seemed to others. For days Maud had been coming home from school full of childish prattle about the lovely things the other girls were going to have. Couldn't she have a real wax doll, with "truly" eyes and hair, that could sing and say mamma ; and a doll house, with kitchen, and a real pump and stove in it, and dining-room and parlor, and lots of lovely bedrooms up-stairs ; and a doll carriage like Mabel Vane's, with blue cushions, and white wheels and body, and umbrella top? She was tired of her old dollies and her broken wagon. Why didn't people ever give her such beautiful things? If she was very good, and wrote to Santa Claus, wouldn't he bring her what she wanted so very, very much? Poor Mrs. Carleton! Do our hearts ever ache over our own troubles as they do over the longings of our little ones? She promised Maud that Santa Claus should bring the very things she craved, and now she knew not how to fulfil her pledge. Commissary and butcher bills were still unpaid, and she so hated to ask even for what was due her! It is such an old, homely, heart-worn story—that of Christmas yearnings that must be unfulfilled! We lay down our cherished plans with a sigh of resignation, but when baby eyes and baby lips are pleading, God forgive us if we are not so humbly patient, if we accept our burden not without a murmur, or yield not without a struggle!

She had other sore perplexities. She well knew she must meet Hal Ransom. Two days had elapsed since Phil had told her of the reception accorded him, and Maud had preferred her complaint against her brother for being so mean to her in not taking the money and giving her a treat.

Heaven! how the widowed soul hugged her boy to her bosom that night, and kissed and blessed and cried over him! Come what might, he should have a Christmas worth remembering, for his remembrance of her! She had long planned to send to Chicago for a handsome suit to replace the worn and outgrown knickerbockers. It would have crushed her to think of her boy's taking money from him, of all people, no matter what the Forties did. Then came the question as to how she would meet him. Go to the fort she had to every day, and meet they must. It was not that he would be obtrusive ; he was too thorough a gentleman for that, and her last letter to him was such that he could not be. It was written in the ecstasy of her bereavement, when she was hiding even from herself the faults and neglects of the buried Philip to whom she had given her girlish love. With lofty spirit she had told him she lived only to teach her children to revere their father's memory, and that she could never think of accepting aid from any one, though she thanked him for the delicacy and thoughtfulness of his well-meant offer. She had asked herself many a time in the last year whether, if it were to be done again, she could find it in her heart to be quite so cold and repellent. She wondered if he had ever heard that the last year of her handsome Philip's life had been devoted more to other women than to her. She could not tolerate the idea that he, above all, should suppose that between Philip and herself all had not been blissful, and that she had been neglected not a little. And yet—and yet was she unlike other women that just now her toilet received rather more thought than usual, and that she wondered would he find her faded —changed ?

They met, as men and women whose hearts hold weightier secrets must meet, with the ease and cordiality which their breeding demands. Scene there

was none ; but she saw, and saw instantly, what she
had vainly striven to teach herself she was utterly indifferent to, that in his eyes she was no more faded
than his love in hers. She could have scourged herself for the thrill of life and youth it gave her.

That night little Philip was hugged closer than
ever. He had been telling her how the captain was
moving into his new quarters, and the children trooped
over there the moment they got back from school, and
would not ask them, because they were infantry, and
Maud cried, and the captain himself came out and took
her in his arms and carried her, and made him come
too, and they all had nuts and raisins and apples, and
the captain was just as kind to them as though they
were cavalry—"more too, for he kept Maudie on his
knee most of the time, and wanted us to stay, but we
had to go and meet mamma. And he said that was
what made him proud of me from the first, because I
was so true to you, mamma," said Phil. "I suppose
because I wouldn't take his half-dollar."

She was silent a moment, pressing her lips to his
cheek, and striving hard to subdue the tears that rose
to her eyes. She had something to ask of her boy
that was hard, very hard. Yet it had to be done.

"You were right, Philip. It would have hurt mamma more than words can tell had you taken money
from—from any one. We are very poor, but we can
be rich in one thing—independence. Mamma has not
had much luck this year. It seemed all to go with
papa's old regiment. But we'll be brave and patient,
you and mamma, and say nothing to anybody about

our troubles. We'll pay what we owe as we go along. Won't we, Phil?"

" I wish I could help some way, mamma."

" You can, my soldier boy."

He looked up quickly and patted her cheek ; then threw his arm around her neck again. Something told him what it would have to be.

"Maudie is a baby who cannot realize our position. Philip is my brave little knight and helper. It—it is so hard for mamma to say it, my boy, but if we buy what she so longs for at Christmas, there will be nothing left for the skates, and I know how you want them, and how many other things you ought to have. You have helped mother so often, Phil. Can you help her once more ?"

For all answer he only clung to her the closer.

And now holiday week was near at hand. It was Friday, and school would close that afternoon, and for two blessed, blissful weeks there would be no session at all. Christmas Day would come on Tuesday, and the Forties were running riot in the realms of anticipation. They hugged each other and danced about the street when the express agent told them of the packages that were coming almost every day for Captain Ransom, and the little Townies, who were wont to protest they were glad their papas weren't in the army, were beginning to show traitorous signs of weakening. It was a sore test, if every regiment had its own Santa Claus, as the Forties said.

And older heads were noting that for some time Captain Ransom drove not so much townward, up the

valley as down; and that there was a well-defined
sleigh track from the lower gate over to the Ranch.
Officers coming up from the stables were quick to note
the new feature in the wintry landscape, and to make
quizzical comment thereon. Then, on Sunday, the
third in Advent, a heavy snow-storm came up during
the morning service, and the wind blew a "blizzard."
It was only a few weeks after the captain's arrival,
but his handsome roans were well known in the valley
already, and the ladies looked at each other and nodded significantly as they saw the team drawn up near
the chapel door when the congregation came shudder-
ing out into the cold. Mrs. Colonel Cross, who had a
charming young sister visiting her for the holidays,
and Mrs. Vane, whose cousin Pansy had come over
from her brother's station at Fort Whittlesey, had
both offered Ransom seats in their pews until he
chose his own; but he had chosen his own very
promptly, and it was well down the aisle opposite
that to which Mrs. Carleton had humbly retired after
her father's death. As a consequence the higher families reached the door only in time to see the captain
bundling the widow and her little ones in his costly
robes, and driving away through the whirling storm.

That night the wind died away; the snow fell heavily, and all the next day it lay in silent, unruffled, un-
furrowed beauty over the broad level below the fort,
and though the captain's sleigh went townward towards evening, and the butcher's "bob" tore an ugly
groove along the lower edge, there was now no trail
other than the foot-path along the willow-fringed

river-bank joining the garrison with the widow's gate.
When Friday came, and the plain was still unfur-
rowed, Fort Rains was unanimous in its conclusion ;
Captain Ransom had offered himself again, and been
rejected.

The households of Vane and Potts, and the ladies,
at least, at the colonel's, breathed freer.   Captain
Ransom was invited to Christmas dinner at all three
places, and begged to be excused.   He explained that
he purposed having all the children at his house from
eight to ten for general frolic that evening—and would
not the ladies come over and see the fun ?   Mrs. Vane
and Pansy were for changing their dinner hour to
five o'clock, if thereby the captain could be secured,
and Vane "sounded" him, but without the hoped-for
result.   He would have to be at home, he said.   Mrs.
Carleton was narrowly watched.   Women who had
been disposed to treat her coldly could have hugged
her now, if they could be sure she had really refused
the best catch in the cavalry, and left a chance for
some one else.   But Mrs. Carleton gave no sign, and
she was a woman they dared not question.   What
staggered the theory of renewed offer and rejection
was the warmth and cordiality of manner with which
they met in public—and they met almost daily.   There
was something that seemed to shatter the idea of rejection in the very smile she gave him, and in the reverence of his manner towards her.   Estrangement there
certainly was none, and yet he had been going over to
the Ranch every day, and his visits had suddenly ceased.
Why ?   They scanned his face for indications ; but,

as Mrs. Vane put it, "he always was an exasperating creature ; you could no more read him than you could a mummy."

Monday before Christmas had come, and Colonel Cross, trudging home from his office about noon, caught sight of the tall and graceful figure of Mrs. Carleton coming towards him along the walk. He was about to hail her in his cheery style, when he saw that her head was bowed, and that she was in evident distress. Even while he was wondering how to accost her, she put him out of doubt. Her lips were twitching and her cheeks were flushed ; tears were starting in her eyes, but she strove hard to command herself and speak calmly.

"You were so kind as to order the 'special' for me this morning, colonel, but I shall not need it—I cannot go to town."

He knew well that something had gone wrong. Blunt, rugged old trooper that he was, he had been her father's intimate in their cadet days, and he wanted to befriend her. More than a little he suspected that hers was not a path of roses among the ladies at Rains. In his presence they were on guard over their tongues, but he had not been commanding officer of several garrisons for nothing.

"Mrs. Carleton," he impetuously spoke, "something's amiss. Can't you tell an old fellow like me, and let me—ah—settle things? Surely it is something I can do."

She thanked him warmly. It was nothing in which he could be of service, she declared, trying hard to smile—she was a little upset and could not go to town. But he saw she had just come from Mrs. Vane's, and he knew that estimable and virtuous woman thoroughly, and drew his conclusions. Whatever was wrong, it was not unconnected with her monitions or ministrations—of that he was confident. As for Mrs. Carleton, she turned quickly from the fort and took her lonely, winding way among the willows to her valley home, a heart-sick woman.

Counting her ways and means, she had found that to pay for the items she had promised Maud and had ordered for her boy—the latter being the suit sent "C. O. D." from Chicago—she would have to ask a favor of her patrons at the fort. She had arranged with the proprietor of the big variety store in town that he should set aside for her a certain beautiful doll and one of the prettiest of the doll carriages and that she would come and get them on this very afternoon. To meet her bills and these expenses, and that there might be no disappointment, she had addressed to the parents of her few pupils a modest little note, enclosing her bill, and asking as a kindness to her that it might be paid by Saturday, the 22d. Courteous and prompt response had come from all but two, and with the money thus obtained she had settled her little household accounts. Mrs. Vane and Mrs. Potts, however, had vouchsafed no reply, and it was to the mothers, not the fathers, her notes had been addressed. On Monday morning, therefore, when she went to give Miss Adèle her lesson, she ventured to ask for Mrs. Potts, and Mrs. Potts was out—spending the day at

13

Mrs. Vane's. So thither she went, and with flushing cheeks and deep embarrassment inquired if the ladies had received her notes. Mrs. Potts had, and was overcome, she said, with dismay. She had totally forgotten, and thought it was next Saturday she meant ; and now the captain had gone to town, and there was no way she could get at him. Then came Mrs. Vane's turn. Mrs. Vane, too, had received her note, but she was not overcome. With much majesty of mien she told the widow that she always paid her bills on the last day of the quarter, and that her husband was so punctilious about it and so methodical that she never asked him to depart from the rule. Mrs. Carleton strove hard to keep down her pride and the surging impulse to cry out against such heartless superiority of manner and management. There was a tinge of reproach in the plea she forced herself to make for her babies' sake. " You know there are no more lessons this term, Mrs. Vane ; my work is done ; and I —so needed it for Christmas, or I would not have asked." And she smiled piteously through the starting tears. Mrs. Vane was sorry—very sorry. She could hardly ask her husband to depart from his lifelong practice, even if he were here—and he, too, had gone to town.

Yes, everybody seemed to have gone or sent to town for Christmas shopping. Her little ones were alone in having no one to buy for them. Harold Ransom too was going, for she saw the handsome roans come dashing up the drive, as she rose, with a burning sense of indignity, to take her leave. She came upon Miss

Pansy in the hallway, all hooded and furred, and beaming with bliss at the prospect of a sleigh-ride to town —behind the roans, no doubt. Never mind that now. Her heart was full of only one thought—her babies. Where were now her long-cherished schemes? All Fort Rains was blithe and jubilant over the coming festivities; Maud was wild with anticipation; and she alone—she alone, who had worked so hard and faithfully that her children might find joy in their Christmas awaking—she alone had seen her hopes turn to ashes. In her pride and her vehement determination to be "beholden" to no one, she would seek no help in her trouble. She went home, asking only to be alone, thankful that the children were spending the day with friends in the garrison, and could not be there to see the misery in her eyes.

Full an hour she gave to her uncontrollable grief, locked in her room, sobbing in utter prostration. Her eyes were still red and swollen; she was weak, trembling, exhausted, when the sudden sound of hoof-beats roused her. The blood flew to her cheeks. Despite her prohibition, then, he was here. He had come again, and something told her he had fathomed her trouble, and would not be denied. She heard the quick, firm tread upon the steps, the imperative rat-tat-tat of the whip-handle on the door. She could have called to her faithful slave Mrs. Malloy, the "striker's" wife, who had known her from babyhood, and bidden her tell the captain she must be excused, but it was too late. Bridget Malloy had seen her face when she came home; had vainly striven to enter her

room and share her sorrow ; had shrewdly suspected
the cause of the trouble, and through the key-hole had
poured forth voluble Hibernian fealty and proffers of
every blessed cent of her savings, but only to be im-
plored to go away and let her have her cry in peace.
Even had Mrs. Carleton ordered her to deny her to
the visitor, it is probable that Mrs. Malloy would have
obeyed—her own instincts.

"Sure it's glad I am to see the captain !" was her
prompt greeting ; " and it was a black day that ever
let ye go from her.   Come right in, an' I'll call her to
ye.   It's all broke up she is."

And so she had to come.   There he stood in the
little sanctuary where Philip in photographed beauty
beamed down upon her from over the mantel, and
Philip's rusting sword hung like that of Damocles by
the fragile thread of sentiment that bound her to the
past.   There he stood with such a world of tenderness,
yearning, sympathy, and suppressed and passionate
love in his dark eyes !   She came in, almost back-
ward, striving to hide her swollen and disfigured face.
He never strove to approach her.   With one hand
on the mantel, he stood gazing sorrowfully at her.
With one hand on the door-knob, with averted face,
she silently awaited his words.

"I have disobeyed you, Kate, though I left my
sleigh and came on Roscoe.   I have tried to accept
what you said eight days ago, but no man on earth
who has heard what I have heard to-day could obey
you longer.   No.   Listen !" he urged, as she half
turned, with silencing gesture.   "I'm not here to

plead for myself, but—my heart is breaking to see you suffering, and to think of your being subjected to such an outrage as that of this morning. Of course I heard of it. I made them tell me. The colonel had seen your distress, and told me you had abandoned the trip to town. I found out the rest. Yes, Mrs. Carleton, if you so choose to term it" (for she had turned with indignant query in her eyes), "I *pried* into your affairs. Do you think I can bear this, to know you are in want—for want it must be, or you'd never have stooped to ask that vulgar, purse-proud, patronizing woman for money? Do you think I can live here and see you subjected to this? By Heaven! If nothing else will move you, in Philip's name, in your children's name, let me lift this burden from you. Send me across the continent if you like. I'll promise to worry you no more, if that will buy your trust. I've lived and borne my lot these eight or nine long years, and can bear it longer if need be. What I can't bear, and won't bear, is your suffering from actual *poverty*. Kate Carleton, won't you trust me?"

"How *can* I be your debtor, Captain Ransom? Ask yourself—ask any one—what would be said of me if I took one cent from you! I *do* thank you. I *am* grateful for all you have done and would do. Oh, it is not that I do not bless you every day and night for being so thoughtful for me, so good to my little ones! It wasn't for myself I was so broken to-day; it was for my—my babies. Oh, I—I *cannot* tell you!"

And now she broke down utterly, weeping hysterically, uncontrollably. In the abandonment of her grief she threw her arms upon the wooden casing of the doorway, and bowed her head upon them. One instant he stood there, his hands fiercely clinching, his broad chest heaving, his bronzed, honest, earnest face working with his weight of emotion, and then, with uncontrollable impulse, with one bound he leaped to her side, seized her slender form in his arms, and clasped her to his breast. In vain she struggled ; in vain her startled eyes, filled with resolute loyalty to the old faith, blazed at him through their mist of tears ; he held her close, as once again, despite her struggles and her forbidding words, he poured forth his plea.

"You *can* take it, you *must* take it. For your own sake, for your children's sake—even for his !—give me the right to protect and cherish you. I—I don't ask your love. Ah, Kate, be merciful !" and then—fatal inspiration !—but the face he loved was so—so near ; he never would have done it had he thought—it was only as utterly unconquerable an impulse as his wild embrace ; his lips were so tremulous with entreaty, with love, sympathy, pleading, pity, passion, everything that impelled and nothing that restrained, that with sudden sweep they fell upon her flushed and tear-wet cheek, and ere he knew it he had kissed her.

There was no mistaking the wrath in her eyes now. She was free in an instant, and bidding him begone. He begged hard for pardon, but to no purpose. She would listen to nothing. Go he must—his presence was insult. And he left her panting with indignation, a vengeance-hurling goddess, a wild-eyed Juno, while he at full gallop went tearing through the snow-drifts, recklessly, dolefully, yet determinedly, back to the post. In half an hour he was whipping to town.

When sunset came, and the evening gun awakened the echoes of the snow-shrouded valley, and the red disk went down behind the crested bluffs far up the stream, a sleigh came out from the fort, and Captain Vane, with curious mixture of cordiality and embarrassment, restored Phil and Maud to the maternal roof, and begged to hand her the amount due from him and from Captain Potts for family tuition. He had only heard a—accidentally—a few minutes before, of her request. And wasn't there something else he could do? Would she not go to town with him to-morrow morning? She thanked him. She hardly knew what to do. Here was the money at last, but it was Christmas eve now, and there was no time to be lost, and town lay full six miles away. Perhaps she wished a messenger now, suggested the captain—he would send in a mounted man gladly. Knowing no other way to secure her treasures for her little ones, she breathlessly accepted his offer, briefly explained the situation, and told him how she longed to have the presents there, with the trifles she had made for them, to greet their eyes with the coming day. The messenger could go to the store and get the coveted doll and carriage; there would surely be sleighs from the fort that would bring them out for him, and he would find the box from Chicago at the express office, and could pay the charges and sign the receipt on her written order to the agent. It was arranged in a moment, and with reviving hope she gave the children their tea and strove to get them early to bed.

Ten o'clock came. The little ones were at last asleep. She had filled the stockings with such inexpensive but loving remembrances as she could afford, and had tottered dangerously near the brink of another flood of tears when Malloy and his wife came in, the one with a box of tools for Phil, the other with a set of china for the doll-house. She had finally bidden those faithful friends good-night, and, having arranged the few gifts she had for the children, she threw over her shoulders a heavy shawl and went to the gate to listen for the messenger's return.

It was a perfect night — clear, still, and sparkling. The moon shone brightly upon the glistening mantle of snow, and tinged with silver the pine crests across the stream. Westward, on a little rise, were the twinkling lights of the fort. Far beyond, far up the narrowing valley, other lights, dim and distant, marked the position of the town. She could hear the faint, muffled sound of shots with which the benighted but jubilant frontiersmen were hailing the coming of the sacred anniversary, like some midwinter Fourth of July, with exuberant and explosive hilarity. Then, nearer at hand, soft, sweet, and solemn, there floated out over the valley the prolonged notes of the cavalry trumpet sounding the signal "Lights out," the "good-night" of the garrison. Then all the broad windows of the barracks were shrouded in sudden gloom; only in the quarters of the officers, on the opposite side of

the parade, were the lights still twinkling. In one of
them, nearest the gate, high up aloft, and close under
the gables, there gleamed a brighter light than all the
others. Even in the chilly air she felt the flush of
blood to her cheeks. That was Ransom's house. She
well knew he had chosen it, farthest from the quarters
and stables of his troop, simply because it was at the
end of the row, overlooking the valley, and nearest
her. Two weeks since he had said to her that he
could not rid himself of the thought of her isolation.
Though off the beaten track a full three-quarter mile,
and within long carbine-range of the sentries, she was
still far away, almost unprotected. Though Indians
were no longer to be feared, there were such things
as tramps and blackguards in the settlements. She
laughed at his fears. She had lived there three years,
and never heard a sound at night other than the occasional howl of a coyote and the distant watch-cry of
the sentries. She had brave old Malloy with his gun,
and Bridget with her tongue and nails; she had Philip's sword, her own brave spirit, and her boy : what
had she to fear?

All the same, struggle against it though she would,
it was sweet to hear his anxious questioning. Even if
unmolested by marauders, something might go wrong
—Maudie have croup, a kerosene lamp burst. She
might need help. Who knew? "I shall put a bright
lamp and reflector in the little round garret window
every night as soon as I get home," he said, "and,
should you ever be in danger or need, throw a red
handkerchief over your biggest lantern, and show it

at the top window. If the sentries don't see it at once, fire Malloy's gun." She promised, laughingly, though repudiating the possibility. She had told herself that Philip's spirit was all the protection she needed; but the night landscape of the valley, the night lights at the fort, had acquired of late an interest they never knew before. She would have scourged herself had she believed, she would have stormed at any one who suggested, that she went to look for his light; but if ever it failed to be there, at ten or eleven or later, she knew it. Whatever might be his evening occupation at the fort — a dinner, a card-party, officers' school, "non-coms.'" recitation—it was his habit on reaching home to go at once to the garret and post his sentinel light. What would he not have given for an answering signal?

And there was the light now. He was home, then, and, despite her anger and his banishment, he was faithful. Christmas eve, and only ten, and he was home and watching over her. She was still quivering with wrath at him for that ravished kiss—at least she told herself she was, and had told him a great deal more. Was it quite fair to drive him from her home, as she had, when Phil was so fond of him and Maudie loved him so, and he was so devoted to them? What could he be doing at home so early? There was a party at the adjutant's, she knew. She had been obliged to decline. She had three invitations for Christmas dinners, and had said no to all, gratefully. There were many who wanted to be kind to her, but she had only one dress she considered fit to wear, so, too, had little Maud, and as for her brave boy Phil, he had nothing—unless the suit from Chicago came in time. Without that he could not go to the captain's Christmas-tree. Why did not the messenger return? She was becoming feverishly anxious.

It was too cold to remain out-of-doors. She re-entered, and paced fitfully up and down her little parlor. She went in and bent over her sleeping children, and rearranged the coverlets with the noiseless touch of the mother's hand; she leaned over and kissed them softly, and now that her surcharged nature had had free vent, and the skies were cleared by the morning's storm, she felt far gentler, happier. Her cry had done her good. Her hopefulness was returning—but not the messenger. What *could* detain him? Where could he be? It was eleven, and long after, when at last she sighted a shadowy horseman loping across the moonlit plain, and slowly he dismounted at her gate and came to her—empty-handed. He was a soldier of Vane's troop, and his tale was doleful. He had been set upon in a saloon, robbed, and beaten. The money was gone, he had brought back nothing but bruises. As consolation he imparted the fact that 'twas too late to get the doll and carriage. The last ones had been sold that evening, as she had not come to claim them. Then he had stepped in to take a drink, because he was cold, and then the catastrophe had occurred. True or false as might be the story, there was no doubt of the veracity of that portion which referred to the drink. Conscious that it was too late to do anything at this hour, she simply dismissed him, bid-

ding him go at once to the post, barred and locked
her door, and sat down, stunned and heartsick. This,
then, was the joyous Christmas for which she had
worked so long and hard! She raised her arms in
one last appeal to Heaven; then threw herself upon
her knees beside her little ones, and buried her face
in her quivering hands. What would their early waking bring to them now but disappointment? For half
an hour she knelt there helpless, stunned. Then lifted
her head—startled.

Somebody was fumbling at the storm-door. With
her heart in her throat, she listened, incredulous, fearful, then convinced. The boards creaked and snapped
beneath a heavy, stealthy tread. She heard, beyond
doubt, a muttered question, a reply. There were two of
them, then! All was darkness in her parlor now, only
the light burned in the children's room. Her heart
bounded, but she stole, despite trembling knees, noise-
lessly into the parlor, stooped and peered through the
slats, and, sure as fate, two men, burly, muffled so that
they were unrecognizable, were bending down at the
storm-house in front of her parlor door. Quickly she
rose, scurried through the parlor, up the stairs to the
room above the kitchen, where she rapped heavily
at the door. "Malloy! Malloy!" she cried. No answer but a snore and heavy breathing. She rattled
the knob and called again. This time with success.

"Who is't?" was the startled challenge.

"It is I—Mrs. Carleton! Quick, Malloy! Two men
are trying to break in at the front door."

She heard the bound with which the old soldier

leaped to the floor. She ran into the front room. One
quick glance showed her Ranscm's signal-light blazing
across the mile of snow. One moment more, and,
muffled in red silk, her biggest lantern swung glowing
in the window. Then down the stairs she hurried to
her children, just as Malloy, with his carbine, and
Bridget, with a six-shooter, swept gallantly into action. She heard his fierce summons, "Who shtands
there?" and listened breathlessly. No response.
"Who's dhere, I say?" Dead silence. Not even
scurrying footsteps. She crept to the window and
peered out. No one near. She raised the sash, threw
open a shutter, and gazed abroad. The little piazza
was deserted, unless both were hiding inside the storm-
house. No! See! Over among the willows by the
stream there are shadowy figures and a sleigh.

"They've gone, Malloy! They are up the river-
bank with a sleigh!" she called. And then she heard
him furiously unbarring the parlor door preparatory
to a rush. She heard it swing open, an impetuous
sally, a collision, a crash, the clatter of a dropped
carbine against the surrounding wood-work, a com-
plication of anathemas and objurgations from the
dark interior, and then a dialogue in choice Hibernian.

"Are ye hurted, Terence?"

"I am. Bad scran to the blagyards that left their
thrunk behind 'em!"

Trunk! what trunk? She bore a light into the parlor, and revealed Malloy, with rueful visage, doubled
up over a big wooden box planted squarely in the

doorway. Robbers, indeed! Mrs. Bridget whisked
him out of the way, ran and closed the children's
door, and in another moment had lugged the big box
into the parlor, and wrenched away the top. The two
women were on their knees before it in an instant.

First they dragged forth a great flat paper box,
damp and cool and moist, and this the widow opened
tremblingly. A flat layer of white cotton, dry; then
paper; a flat layer of white cotton, moist; and then,
peep! Upon the fresh, green coils of smilax, rich with
fragrance, sweet, moist, dewy, exquisite, lay store upon
store of the choicest flowers—rose-buds and rose-blos-
soms in cream and yellow and pink and crimson, car-
nations in white and red, heliotrope and hyacinth, and
fairest pansies, and modest little violets, and gorgeous
tulips, even great callas—the first flowers she had seen
in years. Oh, Captain Santa Claus! who taught you
Christmas wooing? Where learned you such art as
this? Beneath the box was yet another, bearing the
stamp of the great Chicago firm, sealed, corded, just
as he had got it from the agent that evening—Phil's
longed-for suit. She hugged it with delight, while
tears started to her dancing eyes. How good he was!
How thoughtful for her and for her little ones! There,
beneath, was the very white doll-carriage, blue lining,
umbrella top, and all, wherein reposed a wondrous
wax doll, the like of which Maud had never dreamed.
There was a tin kitchen, with innumerable appendages.
There was a glistening pair of club-skates of finest
steel and latest patent, the very thing that Phil so
longed for, and had so lovingly resigned. There were

The publisher regrets that the illustration appearing on this page in the original could not be reproduced satisfactorily and it was therefore eliminated.

fur cap and gloves and boots for him, and such an elegant shawl for Mrs. Malloy! He could send them all he chose, and no offence. But to her—on her he could lavish only flowers.

And then her Irish allies returned to their slumbers, and left her to the rapture of arranging the new presents and the contemplation of her flowers; and she was hugging the big pasteboard box and gloating over her treasures when there was sudden noise without, a rush up the steps, and before she could drop her possessions the door flew open, and in came a wild-eyed, breathless captain of cavalry, gasping the apparently unwarrantable query, "What's the matter?"

For an instant she stared at him in astonishment. Holding tight her flowers, she gazed at his agitated face. "Nothing," she answered. "How could anything be wrong when you have been so—so—" But words failed her.

"Why! your red light's burning" he explained.

"I declare! I forgot all about it!"

Then another silence. He threw himself back in an arm-chair, breathing hard, and trying to recover his composure.

"Do you mean—didn't you mean to signal for help?" he finally asked.

"Yes, I did"—an arch and mischievous smile now brightening her face. "When I swung it I wanted you to come quick and drive—yourself away."

Then she put down her box, and stepped impulsively towards him, two white hands outstretched, tears starting from her eyes, the color surging to her lovely face—"Where can I find words to thank you, Captain Santa Claus?"

He rose quickly, his face flushed and eager, his strong hands trembling.

"Shall I tell you?" he asked.

Her head was drooping now; her eyes could not meet the fervent love and longing in his; her bosom heaved with every breath. She could only stand and tremble when he seized her hands.

"Kate, will you take back what you said to-day?"

She stole one glance into his passionate, pleading eyes, and her head drooped lower.

"*Can't* you take it back, Kate?"

A moment's pause. At last the answer. "How can I, unless—unless you take back what you—what caused it?"

Never before had the little Carletons waked to such a radiant Christmas morning. Never had the Forties known so royal a Christmas-tree. Never before was "Uncle Hal's" so thronged with beaming faces and happy hearts. But among all the little ones whom his love and thoughtfulness had blessed there was no face that shone with bliss more radiant, with joy more deep and perfect, than that of Captain Santa Claus.

"CAPTAIN SANTA CLAUS."

THE MYSTERY OF 'MAHBIN MILL.

CHAPTER I.

PLACID and homelike enough were all its surroundings, one would say. It seemed the very last place to look for romance or mystery—the very last place in the world to be confronted by a foul and savage crime. There was not a shadow on the bright, breeze-ruffled mill-pond whereon the ducks were splashing and quacking noisily. Not a willow drooped its mourning branches over the sunny shallows above, or the foaming, rushing, tumbling torrent below the dam. Not a tree with heavy, spreading foliage stood guard between the sunshine and the shores. Nothing but a few pert, sturdy young hickories fringed the banks, bolt upright in the broad glare of the noontide, and proclaiming in their very attitude their detestation of all that was vague, dark, or shadowy. There were no beetling cliffs—no firs, no pines, no dark hemlocks—nothing in the least suggestive of gloom or tragedy. The valley lay broad and open. Cosy homesteads and cottages gleamed here and there along the slopes, nestled in little groves of their own. Orchards, a vineyard, many fields of waving, yellowing grain, broad pastures dotted with drowsy sheep and drowsier, clover-fed cattle ; bright green patches every now and then where the sugar-maples huddled together in rustling gossip; and smiling farms and winding, well-kept country roads lay north and south. Westward, a few hundred yards, the gleaming bosom of the island-dotted lake into which the mill-stream poured its swirling waters; eastward, a short mile, the roofs and chimneys of the thriving county town; and then, over towards the distant railway, a creamy spire, with the sacred emblem of the cross glinting and shimmering in the sunlight, peeped through the fringe of waving tree-tops. All was quiet, rural beauty. All told of peace, life, contentment, and prosperity this lovely July morning of the centennial year—all save the hush and awe that hung about old 'Mahbin mill.

Over by the waste weir, with musical splash and laughter and faint little clouds of spray, a tumbling sheet of water was disappearing into the cool depths below; but here, in the broad, beaten roadway around the worn threshold, was impressive silence. The busy whir and hum and clatter was all stilled, though elsewhere this had been a bustling Monday morn. Men spoke in low, awe-stricken whispers, and went on tiptoe over the creaking floor within. Peace and contentment, life and prosperity, flooding sunshine, laughing-water, merry-throated birds made glad the scene around; but within was silence and mystery and death. Here, prone on the flour-dusted floor of the old office lay all that was mortal of gray-haired Sam Morrow, the miller, murdered by murder most foul, as one and all could see; and young Dick Graham, his right-hand man for years, had gone, gone no one knew whither.

In all its peaceful history, Nemahbin had known no such sight or sensation as this. Thirty years had the old mill been the rallying-point of the farmers, to the exclusion of the attractions of the tavern in the little town. Morrow was a character—a man who read and remembered, a man who took the papers and had an opinion, backed by good reasoning, of public men and public affairs of the day. He grew to be an authority on many and most subjects, but he never grew to be popular. Morrow had an ugly temper when crossed, a lashing, venomous tongue when angered, and, of late, there had been growing up among the farmers who drove thither with their grain a suspicion that old Sam, in his grasping, money-loving greed had become unscrupulous. In this there was rank injustice. Crabbed and ill-tempered as the man had often been, surly and rough of speech as he had become, there did not live a more rigidly honest man—his word was his bond. His own dealings were beyond question, and six months before his death no man within a thirty-mile radius of Nemahbin had ever been heard to hint at such a thing as sharp practice at 'Mahbin mill.

He had not been a happy man. His home life had been far from sweet and peaceful. Ten years ago his patient and devoted wife had died—worn out, some neighbors were good enough to say, by his outbreaks of fury and his cutting injustice. But he had loved her, loved her well, and he mourned her bitterly. Two children she had left him : one a son, high-spirited, impulsive, and wilful, between whom and his father there waged incessant feud while he was at home, and between whom and that same father there passed frequent letters of most loving description when the boy was placed at boarding-school. Young Sam had been liberally provided for when he went away, and his pocket-money was unstinted. The boy was not vicious, but the restraints of school discipline seemed to tempt him from one mad exploit to another, and, after two years of sorely tried patience, the authorities of the school requested his withdrawal. Sam was fifteen then, a bright, quick-witted fellow, a leader in all boyish sports and mischief, and immensely popular among the farm folk around Nemahbin. His chum and intimate friend from early boyhood had been Dick Graham; like himself, an only son of an idolizing mother, but, unlike himself, compelled to labor for her support. When young Sam had been sent away to school after his mother's death, the old man was noticed on several consecutive days hovering uncertainly about the little country store where his boy's friend was working from morn till night doing hard jobs and thankfully carrying home his scanty wages at the end of the week. One day he blustered in on the "boss" with brief ceremony:

"Murphy," said he, "you work that boy too hard, and pay him too little. If you don't double his wages, I will, and take him out to the mill to boot." Murphy was vastly angered at the proceeding, and Murphy's adherents voted around the fire that night that old Sam Morrow had no business to be "spilin' the market for boys," and undermining other folk's concerns in that way; but the miller stuck to his word; Murphy would not agree, and at the end of the month Dick Graham moved out to the mill, where his bright face, and cheery, alert ways, soon deepened the interest old Sam felt in him for his own boy's sake. Then he moved Mrs. Graham out there, and placed her and her boy in the cottage near the mill-house, as his own home was termed. And then the minister of the pretty church over towards the railway had come over to call on Mr. Morrow—who was not of the fold—and to shake hands with him, and when he went away he bent down and kissed pretty little Nellie—the miller's only daughter, and his darling—and had asked that his own little girls might come over to make her acquaintance and to gather pond lilies. All this had happened ten years back, when Nellie was a blue-eyed, sunny-haired child, and Sam was in his first turbulent year at school.

Little Nell had to go to her own school very soon. It lay across country over where the minister lived, and many was the time in the rough spring weather when Dick Graham had to carry her over the rushing brooks that burst across the roadway from the deep-drifted slopes of snow. He was a splendid, sturdy boy of fifteen then—manly, truthful, independent; and loyally he strove to serve his benefactor in the clattering old mill, and still more loyally he watched over the bonny child who seemed that master's all in all.

Things went smoothly enough, in all conscience, a year or two. Dick trudged off to evening school during the wintry season, and had found a good friend

in that same minister, who lent him books and helped
him along in his studies; but then Sam came home,
virtually expelled from school, and then began a series of domestic troubles between father and son that
brought sorrow and anxiety to all. Old Sam in his
wrath would taunt the boy with having disgraced him,
and young Sam in his flush of temper would threaten
to quit his father's home for good and all. Dick
strove to reason with his friend, but the boy was sensitive and stung to the quick. A kind word, a loving
touch from his father would have melted his heart in
an instant. He would have gone back to school full
of apology and promises to amend; but his father's
eyes were averted and his tongue edged with fire.
Sam swore it was of no use to try and be patient.
Then Dick went to the minister in his perplexity, and
that worthy gentleman came strolling over to the
mill, and looking over the ground, so to speak. His
was a diplomatic mind, and it had reason to be. It
was easy to win the son's confidence. He, Dick, and
Sam junior soon formed a trio of fast friends, and before long another scheme was broached; and, with
some surly misgiving on old Morrow's part, Sam was
sent to another and larger school. It was the old
man's hobby that his boy should be well educated.
But a plethora of pocket-money, said the authorities
of the first establishment, had been the cause of his
downfall, and now the old man sternly refused to give
his son a cent. All his expenses were to be met and
paid, and the principal of the new school was to give
him a certain trifling sum on holidays. There was no

known trouble for a year as the result of this arrangement. The boy felt that he had amends to make and
so did his best. A widowed sister of old Morrow had
come to his home and taken charge of it and little
Nell, and there was another era of comparative peace.

But to young Sam the school life was far from
bright. Stinted now where he had formerly been
indulged, he found himself forced into a position
greatly contrasted with the prominence and popularity he had enjoyed among the youngsters of the year
before. He was beginning to learn the lesson that
sooner or later saddens and often embitters the brightest minds—the lesson that even here in free America
money is the standard of even personal value. It was
not so with Western boys before the war. Money was
a thing well-nigh unknown to them, but the "flush"
days brought with them new ideas, and the ideas stuck
fast long after the flush days had gone. Sam Morrow
found that he was no longer the pet of the "best set."
Money and reckless good-nature had won it for him
in the old school; good-nature unbacked by money
was no help here at the new. Sam said nothing to
his father, but his letters to Dick became more frequent. He stood to his work like a little man, and
despite the sorrow and loneliness of that year he came
home the better for it all. He had made excellent
progress. His teacher had praised him; the minister
put him through his paces and extolled him; and old
Morrow, proud and pleased, wanted to unbend and
send the boy back for his second year with some substantial token of his pleasure; but stubborn pride on

both sides seemed to stand between father and son. Sam junior would ask nothing, and the old man's reply to the minister's well-meant suggestion was, "Well, if the boy wants money now let him come and say so." And this Sam swore he would not do, and so it ended.

Next year there was a catastrophe. Sam was now a stalwart, handsome young fellow of seventeen. "Ready to go to college," said his teachers. One day old Morrow received a telegraphic despatch begging him to come at once to the school. He went, and in four days was home again with Sam and a broken heart. Small sums of money had been missed from time to time by various pupils of the school. Suspicion had fastened on a sharp boy who was believed to spend more money than he legitimately received. A watch was kept, a search was made, and Sam Morrow was detected passing at a store some of the marked money. Questioned as to where he got it, he for the time declined to answer, until told that he was suspected of the theft. He then confessed that it was part of a small sum Fielding, the sharp boy aforementioned, paid him from time to time for translating his Cæsar for him. Fielding promptly, and with much apparent indignation, denied the story. Receiving such assistance and passing off another boy's work as his own was an offence for which a pupil was always severely punished. The case rested as a question of veracity between the two boys, with the odds vastly in favor of Sam—for a few hours only, pending further investigation, but that investigation was fatal. At least twelve dollars of the missing

money was found secreted in Sam's books and clothing. He had furiously denied everything ; he protested in vain that he had no idea how it came there,
but his lonely, solitary ways were remembered, his
habits of hanging about the dormitories apparently
at study when the boys were at play—and there was
no one to stand up for him. Old Morrow came, listened in crushed silence, and took his boy home. Honest
to the backbone himself, he was sore stricken to think
that his son should steal. He had heard first the stories
of the teachers and pupils before being ushered into
the presence of the accused. All hot impulse and fury,
he had come upon his lonely and friendless son, and
when the poor fellow, bursting into tears in his misery
and excitement of the moment, had thrown his arms
about his father's neck, sobbing, "I have not done it,
I am innocent," he had sternly unclasped the pleading
hands and ordered him to prepare at once to go home
with him. Sam seemed utterly stunned by his father's
refusal to hear a word. He was almost crazed with
misery when he reached home. The minister and
Dick listened to his story and believed it. Old Sam
shut himself up; refused to see any one for some days,
until Nellie's tears and petitions secured a brief interview for the worthy churchman. This time the latter
was not diplomatic. He believed the boy wronged
from beginning to end. He told old Morrow in so
many words that his pride and stubbornness were
sin and shame, and roused the old man to such a pitch
of wrath that he shrieked out his hope that the son
who had disgraced him might never come before his

sight again—and he never did. Sam Morrow heard the furious words. Pride came to his aid; and never saying a word of farewell to the friends whom he knew would strive to dissuade him, but clinging long to sweet twelve-year-old Nellie, and sobbing as though his heart would break, Sam left his father's roof that night. Five years had passed away, and not one word was ever heard from him. The old man's curse had indeed come home to rest; his fading eyes were never more to be blessed by the sight of his son.

But this was only half of his misery. The minister left the house with his-blood up; went forthwith to that school and was closeted some hours with his old friend the principal. Sam's side of the story had an intelligent advocate; a revulsion of feeling had set in; boys and men both began to recall good points about Morrow that had not occurred to them before, and queer things about that fellow Fielding. In less than a month after Sam's disappearance there came a letter to old Morrow one day which he read in gasping amaze, and then fell prone and senseless on the floor of the very office where he lay now prone and dead. Sam's story was true; Fielding had confessed even to having stolen the money and hiding portions of it in Sam's property, to divert suspicion from himself.

But now came a long illness in which old Morrow lay at death's door. He raved for his boy. He cursed his own mad folly and injustice. He did everything that could be suggested to bring the wanderer home again. The story went into the papers. Advertisements were circulated through the Western States.

Even detectives were called upon, but to no purpose.
Sam never returned. The old man, bent and sorrowing, but with as fiery a temper and an even more en-
venomed tongue, seemed to live only for Nellie's sake
and the hope of once more greeting his boy. Nellie
herself had spent some years at boarding-school and
had grown into a lovely girl of eighteen. Dick Graham was a fine, manly fellow, good to look at and
better to trust and tie to. "Too good a man to stay
grubbing for old Morrow at the mill," said the neighbors. "Far too valuable and intelligent for the humble stipend that is paid him," said the minister. "Old
Morrow" had grown miserly and grasping, said Public
Opinion—and it was true. He had no confidant; he
had no friends to whom he could open his heart. In
dumb sorrow he shrank from the world, ever looking
with haggard eyes for some trace of the lost boy
whom his injustice and cruelty had driven into exile.
Nellie was his one comfort. He gloried in her bud-
ding beauty, but he meant to make a lady of her, and
even during her school vacation she did not always
come home. It was too lonely and sad a spot for one
so bright as she, said the old man, and he willingly
permitted her to visit school friends in their city
homes, and went month after month to see her—and
bear to her, and the friends she liked, huge and uncouth offerings of candy or flowers in his efforts to
show his appreciation of their interest in his precious
child. Nellie was a princess in his eyes, but others
saw in her a somewhat spoiled and over-petted beauty.
That is—some others—most others. There was one

who worshipped her as even her father never dreamed of doing; one to whom her faintest wish was law; one to whom her lightest word was sacred, and to whom her smile, or the touch of her little hand meant heaven. People wondered how Dick Graham could consent to hang on there at 'Mahbin mill, "grubbing" for that grasping old Morrow like a slave. Poor Dick! Slave he was, as many another had been, but not the miller's. He could and would have broken with him three years before, when the death of his invalid mother left the young fellow independent of all claim—but he could not and would not break the tie that bound him to 'Mahbin and the dusty, dingy, red-shingled old mill. He idolized Nellie Morrow, and she held his life in her hands.

She had learned to be very fond of Dick in the year that followed her brother's disappearance. She had grown into his heart the year before she went to school, and when she came home from her first vacation, child though she was, she knew it and gloried in it. Each year added to her maidenly graces, and to his thraldom, and the very winter that preceded this centennial summer Dick had brought her home from a sleighing-party one night fairly wild with joy and pride. In answer to his impetuous and trembling words she had murmured to him that he was dearer to her than anybody else could be, and he believed it, though Miss Nellie had grave doubts in her own mind as to the truth of that statement even when she made it. Still, it was very nice to have the best-looking and smartest young man in and around 'Mahbin for

her own, when she was home, but he was not quite
to be compared with the exquisites she saw in the
city streets, or the brothers of some of her school
friends.   And there was one—oh! so romantic a fellow! whom she met that very winter in Chicago when
spending Thanksgiving holidays with a schoolmate;
a dark-eyed, splendid-looking man, tall, straight, ath-
letic, with bronzed features and such a strange history! He was much older than these school-girls. He
must have been thirty or thereabouts, and was own
cousin to her friend.   He had been a soldier when
very young; had run away from home and fought
in the great war, and had been a wanderer almost ever
since; had been to California and to sea, and—they
did not really know where else.   Nellie was too young
to notice that he had not been cordially welcomed
by the old people on his arrival at the home of her
friend.   He had been wild and reckless, had "Cousin
Harry," and papa did not like him, was the explanation of subsequent coldness she could not help seeing.
But to the girls he was perfect.   He had so mournful,
mysterious, pathetic a manner.   He was trying so
hard to find some steady employment—was so eager
to settle down—and he soon became so interested in
Nellie, so devoted to her in fact, and the very day
they returned to school—how it came about she never
knew exactly, his sympathetic manner did it, perhaps,
—she told him about her brother and his utter disappearance, and then she wondered at the sudden eager
light in his eyes, the color that shot into his face
through bronze and all, and the unmistakable agita-

tion with which he had asked the question, "What
was his name?" For an instant she believed he must
have met Sam and known him, but this he denied,
denied even when he asked to see his photograph.

Then "Cousin Harry" had been searching in his
questions about Nellie, her father, his age, his property, her prospects. It was easy enough to extract
all manner of information from her school-girl friend,
and, when Nellie went back to school, she had reason
to believe there was something very real in Mr. Henry
Frost's decided interest in her.

She knew Dick loved her. She had given him every
reason to hope that she was growing to care for him;
yet before the Christmas holidays she twice had more
reason to remember Harry Frost's devoted manner—
and when she started home for those very holidays
he was on the train.

It was Christmas eve that sent Dick Graham home
happier than he had ever been in his life, but in one
short week the happiness had fled. Mr. Frost had
taken up his abode at the little tavern in the village;
had acquired some strange influence over old Morrow,
and was playing the devoted to Nellie in a way she
too plainly liked. Early in January she went back
to school, but Frost remained. He had indeed gained
a powerful influence over the lonely old man—no one
knew how—for Morrow invited the stranger to his
house to stay awhile, and, before January was over,
the tall, dark-eyed, dark-haired, athetic man was occupying a desk in the office of the old mill.

There was great speculation and conjecture and

gossip all around 'Mahbin over this matter. The mill had been doing rather less business than usual; no additional men were needed. The office required little attention, for old Morrow had kept his own books and done his own letter-writing for years. If a clerk were needed, why take in a stranger whom nobody knew, they urged, when there was young Graham, whom everybody liked and trusted? And yet, before spring had fairly set in, old Morrow had turned over his book-keeping and writing to this Mr. Frost; and though the key of the little safe was never intrusted to any hand but that of the master, and though there was one desk no one but Morrow himself could open, Frost was soon as much at home in the mill as though he had lived there a lifetime.

When the brief Easter holiday came an odd thing happened. Nellie Morrow declined to go with any of her school-friends. She wrote that she wanted to see dear old 'Mahbin again, and delightedly the miller brought her home. It was a week of torment to poor Dick Graham; a holiday that proved far from satisfactory to Morrow, for he saw with sudden start that his bonny Nell was becoming vastly interested in Mr. Frost, whom he was beginning to distrust.

When Frost had come to Nemahbin, in December, he had sought the old miller, requested a confidential interview, told him, with all apparent frankness, of his meeting with Nellie at the home of his uncle, near Chicago, and of her telling him the sad story of Sam's disappearance.

"Mr. Morrow," said he, "I believe I met and knew

15

your son on the Pacific coast. What is more, I believe I can find him." The miller knew that Frost's
relations were people of high position, but did not
know that the man before him was very far from
standing well in their esteem. But he had been im-
posed upon more than once by people who sought to
make money from his eagerness to obtain any clue
to the whereabouts of his missing boy. He closely
questioned Frost, and was speedily convinced that
there was no imposition here. He had known him,
and known him well; for, even in little tricks of speech
and manner, Frost could describe Sam to the life. The
old man's first impulse was to take Frost with him and
start for the Pacific coast at once; but the latter pointed out to him that the journey to mid Arizona was
very long and expensive, and that he had reason to
believe Sam had left there and gone with miners to
Montana. He had friends and correspondents; he
would write; he did write, and showed Morrow the
letters, and they went apparently to Prescott, Arizona, but not for three months did answers come; and
then they were vague and indefinite, and meantime
the old man's heart had been torn with suspense and
anxiety, and he rebelled at the restriction placed upon
him by Frost, that he should admit to nobody that
they were on the trail of his absent son—that Frost
had known him well " in the mines," as he said, though
by another name. He disliked it still more that there
was so much of his own life while in the distant West
of which Frost gave varying accounts, and always
avoided speaking; and now it was plain that he was

"making up" to Nellie; it was plain that she was far from averse to the attentions of this handsome and distinguished fellow, with his air of reserve and mystery; and it was plain that poor Dick Graham was both miserable and suspicious. He had been set against Frost from the very first.

Still there was a certain element with whom he had attained popularity—the young men about the village, and especially those of the large and thriving town over on the railway. He was a superb horseman, and had ridden with grace and ease a horse that poor Dick had pronounced utterly unmanageable. Then, one night during the Easter holidays, a large party of the young people of Nemahbin had driven over to town to attend the ball given by a local military organization. Nellie was the belle on the occasion, and was coquetting promiscuously with the officers and the members of the company, evidently to the annoyance of that hitherto unrivalled Mr. Frost. Even gloomy Dick Graham found some comfort in this, but his comfort gave way to dismay when, after a brief and rather clumsily executed drill of his command, the captain had suddenly turned over his sword to Mr. Frost, and the latter, as though by previous arrangement, stepped forward, and, with all the ease of an expert tactician and drill-master, and with stirring, martial voice and bearing, put the company through one evolution after another with surprising rapidity, and finally retired, the applauded and envied hero of the occasion. Nellie had monopolized him the rest of the evening, and all men held him in great esteem. Questioned as to his wonderful proficiency, he laughingly answered, "Why I soldiered through the last two years of the war in the volunteers, and saw a good deal of the regulars afterwards, out West—that is, I used to watch them with great interest," and quickly changed the subject.

But Dick Graham's jealous eyes—and no eyes are so sharp as those whose scrutiny is so whetted—marked that he had changed color, and that his manner was nervous and embarrassed. From that day on he watched Frost like a cat.

June came in with sunshine and roses, and a great centennial celebration and exhibition in the far East, and a great convention for the nomination of a president, and the country was so taken up with these stirring events that, when June went out, precious little attention was paid to an affair that, a year earlier or later, would have thrilled the continent with horror. In one short, sharp, desperate struggle of a quarter of an hour, Custer, the daring cavalry leader of the great war—Custer, the yellow-haired, the brave, the dashing, the hero of romance and fiction and soldierly story—Custer and his whole command had been swept out of existence by an overwhelming force of Indians.

Nellie was home again, and Frost was now occupying a room in Sam Morrow's little house. The old man had come to Dick but a short time before her return, and, with something of his old kind and confidential way, had said to him that Frost was to remain with them but a few weeks longer, and that he was unwilling to have him under the same roof with Nellie even during that little while. Morrow had begun to look on Frost as a liar. He felt certain that he had known his lost boy, but doubted now his pretensions as to his ability to find him. Indeed, Frost admitted that he had lost the clue, and it was at this time that Morrow at last told the minister of the matter. That he was being deceived in more ways than one the old man was convinced, yet had nothing tangible to work upon; but his worst suspicions had not really done justice to the facts in the case. Morrow would have killed the man could he have known the truth—that he knew well just where the missing son was to be found, and would not tell—and that, virtually robbing the old miller of one child, he had now well-nigh robbed him of the other. Between him and Nellie letters had secretly passed, at regular intervals, ever since the Christmas vacation. She was fascinated, yet she, too, distrusted. He swore that he loved her—longed to make her his wife—yet forbade her confessing to her father that such was the case. More than that, he had cautioned her to look for an indifferent manner on his part on her return. He explained that her father disliked him, and would send him away instantly if their love were suspected. He even urged her to encourage Dick Graham. He was playing a desperate game, indeed. He had hoped to win the father's confidence with the daughter's love, and secure his consent—and blessing—and fortune; but, as matters stood, he knew that, though he might win Nellie, it would be in defiance of the father's will, and that meant disinheritance and banishment for both.

By every art in his power he had striven, of late, to
curry favor with Graham, but without success.   Dick
was coldly civi¹ and would have been thankful for an
excuse at open rupture.   He suspected Frost of having won Nellie away from him, but could prove absolutely nothing.   He believed him to be a mere advent-
urer, and had urged the miller to write to those con-
nections of whom he had boasted—the Chicago relatives — and ascertain his history ; but Morrow had
sternly silenced him with the information that he
knew it all—at least he knew enough.   "Mr. Frost
is here for a purpose, and it is sufficient that I have
brought him here," was the old man's reply to further
objections, and so poor Dick felt that nothing more
was to be said.

But with Nellie's return came a revival of hope.
She was sweeter, prettier than ever, and her manner
to Dick was now as gentle, and even confidential, as
it had been careless and indifferent during the late
winter.   She came home about the 15th of June, and
for the fortnight that followed it was Dick, not Mr.
Frost, whom she seemed to favor.   Graham hardly
dared believe the evidence of his senses, but was too
blissful to analyze matters.   The old man, of late, had
taken to spending some hours in the evening down
at his office in the mill, and Frost was generally closeted there with him.   Very surly and sad and irasci-
ble the miller had grown.   He was bitter and unjust
to everybody.   Several times he had angrily repri-
manded Graham in the presence of customers and
mill-hands for things that were entirely of Frost's do-

ing. There had been errors in the accounts, over
which the farmers had growled not a little ; and one
day, bursting from a group of men who had been calling his attention to a matter of the kind, the old man
stamped furiously into the office, shut the door after
him with a bang, and was heard to say, in loud and
angry tones, to some one, " Now the next time this
happens, by God, you go !"

A moment after, Dick Graham came from the office
into the mill, and that night it was told in Nemahbin
that the old man had threatened to discharge him.
He and Graham seemed to get along very badly, and
no man could explain it.

But, gaining hope from Nellie's smiles, Dick was
ready to bear up against the old man's fit of rage.
At heart, he knew the miller liked and trusted him.
There was much he could not fathom, but was content
to wait and watch. Meantime he kept his eye on
Frost—noted how nervous and ill at ease he was becoming, marked his labored attempts to win his friendship, and withheld it the more guardedly.

One day, about a week after Nellie's return, business required that he and Frost should go together to
the neighboring town on the railway. They were
standing by the elevator on a side-track with a knot of
young men, when a train came rumbling in from the
East, and as it drew up at the station it was seen that
the rear car was filled with soldiers.

" Hello !" shouted one of the party.   " Let's go and
have a look at the regulars." Dick started with the
rest, but suddenly stopped.   An indefinable sensation

prompted him to look around for Frost, and Frost
was nowhere to be seen. Turning quickly back, he
entered the open doorway of the little warehouse, and
there, in a dark corner, peering through a knot-hole
over towards the station, was his mysterious compan-
ion. Dick approached him on tiptoe, and clapped him
sharply on the shoulder.

"Come, man! come and see the soldiers; some of
your friends may be there."

White as death was Frost's face as he turned with
fearful start. Then, seeing it was Graham, and sus-
pecting it was a trick, he flushed crimson, and angrily,
though with trembling lips, replied,

"My friends! what do you mean? How the devil
should I have friends among them? Go yourself, if
you want to see them, but leave me alone."

And Graham turned away, more than ever convinced
that, in some way, Frost's knowledge of soldiering was
derived from personal experiences he wished to con-
ceal.

A week more, and he had another opportunity of
testing it. Going to the village for the mail, he found
a group of men eagerly listening to one of their number who was reading aloud the terrible details of the
Custer massacre. Graham heard it all in silence, got
the mill mail, and walked thoughtfully homeward.
Old Morrow was seated with Nellie in the porch, and
Frost, hat in hand, was standing at the foot of the
steps, looking up at them as he spoke deferentially to
the miller.

"Any news, Dick?" asked the miller, shortly.

"Terrible news, sir!" said Graham, eying Frost closely as he spoke. "General Custer and his regiment, the Seventh Cavalry, were butchered by the Indians a fortnight ago."

Frost fairly staggered. A wild light shot into his face; his hat fell from his nerveless hand.

"I do not believe a word of it!" he gasped. "It's a lie! They never could! Give me the paper," he demanded, hoarsely; but Graham coolly avoided his attempt to seize it and handed the paper to Morrow. Eying him closely, as Dick had done, the miller tore the wrapper with provoking deliberation, and finally gave the contents to Frost. He had partially recovered self-control by this time, but his hands shook like palsy as he unfolded the paper.

"My God! it's true! — mainly true, at least," he gasped, while drops of sweat started to his forehead. "All with him were killed. It has knocked the breath out of me. I knew so many of them out there, you know."

"In Arizona?" asked Morrow.

"Ye - yes — Arizona!" he stammered. "It tells here what officers were killed, but does not give the names of the men. I wish it did. I wish I knew. They are the ones I saw most of." Then he stopped short, as though he had said too much. And all the time both Morrow and Graham had never ceased their rigid scrutiny, and he knew it. He hurriedly went away.

CHAPTER III.

THAT night Nellie was fitful and constrained in manner. Dick went home restless and unhappy. It was very late, but there was the light burning brightly down at the office.

"Who are there?" he asked the lad who did odd jobs around the miller's house, and who slept in Graham's cottage.

"Mr. Morrow and Frost. Gosh! how the old man has been cussin' him. He cusses everybody round here now, don't he? I heerd down in the village you was going to quit."

Graham made no reply, but turned gloomily into his own room.

Next morning Frost came to him looking very pale and nervous.

"Graham," he said, "I want to ask a great favor. I must go to Chicago, and I want twenty dollars. Will you lend me that much? I will give it to you again next week."

"Why do you come to me?" asked Graham, shortly.

"The old man and I are at loggerheads, and—I know he would not let me have it. Once in Chicago, and I can get money, you shall have it—sure."

Graham hesitated. He had saved but little from

the small stipend allowed him, but a thought struck him that the surest way to get rid of an objectionable acquaintance was to lend him money. It might keep Frost from returning. Stepping to his worn old desk, he unlocked and opened it, took from an inner compartment a small roll of bills, counted out twenty dollars, and handed it to Frost without a word.

"You think you won't get this back, Graham, but you will," said the latter, as he eagerly took it and went away. This was a Tuesday morning. On the following Sunday Dick Graham was amazed to see Frost standing at the miller's gate talking earnestly with Nellie, who dropped her head and scurried into the house as she caught sight of his approaching form.

"Back, you see!" said Frost, holding out his hand, which Dick unwillingly took. He had returned a new man. His clothes, that had begun to grow shabby, were replaced by new ones of stylish cut and make; his eyes were bright, his color high, his voice ringing and animated; his manner was brisk and cheery, yet nervous.

"Have you seen Mr. Morrow?" was all Graham could find to say by the way of welcome. "He is down at the mill, and wants you."

It had been a wretched five days for Dick. Twice he had surprised Nellie in tears that she could not explain, and the old man had treated him with gross injustice on several occasions. All his old fury of manner had been redoubled. He openly accused Dick of having furnished money to aid Frost in getting away when he knew him to be a cheat and an impostor; knew that Frost had garbled the accounts and been stealing at the mill, and in all probability he was no better than an accomplice.   Twice Dick's indignation and wrath had given way to angry retort, and the story had gone far and wide around Nemahbin that the old man and the young one were bitter enemies, and Dick had openly vowed he could stand it no longer.   Then Nellie, who had been coquetting with his hopes and fears, had once again plunged him into the depths.   He loved her blindly, madly, poor fellow, and was bent as she willed, but the time had come when he could brook his ills no longer ; and that Sunday evening, standing by the rushing stream down below the dam, and moodily throwing stone after stone into the dark waters, Dick Graham had determined to face his fate, and have the matter ended then and there.

He was to take her to the village for evening service.   She and her aunt quite frequently spent the night with friends in 'Mahbin in preference to coming back to the mill through the darkness, and this bright July day had turned to night, dark, cloudy, overcast, with heavy fog-wreaths whirling through the cheerless air.   The rain came pattering down as they left the church, and hospitable friends urged their stay. Ten minutes later Dick was standing in the bright light of a parlor, face to face with the girl who had been his idol from boyhood until now.   They were alone.   She saw in his face that the crisis had come, and was pale and nervous as he was pale and determined, yet she strove to assume a light and laughing manner.

"What is it, Dick? You have been solemn as an undertaker for a whole week, and to-night you are like—I don't know what."

Quickly he seized her hands, and held them firmly against every effort to draw them away. His heart beat like a hammer, his eyes were flaming with the fire of his love, his lips quivered and twitched with the intensity of his emotion.

"Nellie," he said, "I can stand it no longer! That man is back again; I saw you with him to-day. I— oh!—time and again I have told you how I loved you. It is more than love—it is worship, almost. It has been so ever since you were a little girl and I carried you to school. You did care for me—you know you did—until this fellow came here and made us all wretched. Nellie, I will have an answer to-night. I will know if you love me; tell me, tell me now." It was no longer an imploring prayer, it was a demand.

Struggle though she might, she could not free herself. His eyes seemed to burn into hers, and she shrank from their wild gaze as though they stung to her very soul.

"Answer me," he said. "You told me you loved me last Christmas. Do you love me now?"

"Oh, Dick, I—I didn't know. I could not tell," she gasped; "I thought I loved you, but—"

"But now you know you love him, is it?" he almost hissed. "Do you know what I think of him? He is a scoundrel, a man without home or name. He has a history he dare not tell; he lies every time he

answers a question; he wants to marry you because
you will be rich, but that's all."

"You shall not speak of him so," she interrupted
in wrath and indignation. "He is a gentleman, and
he does love me, and all you say of him is false. I
know he has been unhappy, unfortunate—"

"He has been more than that, I'll be bound," sneered
Graham, all bitter, jealous anger now. "He is a criminal of some kind—mark my words."

"How dare you?" she cried; "oh, how dare you?
He would crush you if you would dare speak so to
him. I will never forgive you—never. I never want
to see or speak to you again—"

"What do you say?" he gasped, livid with pain
and misery.

"I never want to see or speak to you again," she
repeated, though her eyes quailed before the dumb
agony of his. For a moment there was dead silence.
Then with one long look in her paling face he said,
slowly, almost humbly:

"I take you at your word. Life has been hell to
me here for a long time, and you—you, whom I loved
—have driven me from the only home I ever had."

One instant more and he was gone, leaving her sobbing wildly, she hardly knew why.

And early next morning came the fearful news that
her father lay murdered at the mill.

A week of intense excitement followed. Not only
in Nemahbin was the mysterious death of old Morrow
the one subject of conversation; but all through the
surrounding counties people talked of nothing else.

By sunset of that beautiful Monday the news had spread far and wide ; the reporters of the city journals were already on the spot, and by Tuesday night the verdict of the coroner's jury had gone forth and the officers of the law were in search of the criminal, whose name flashed over the humming wires from one ocean to another.   Richard Graham stood accused of the murder of his employer, and Richard Graham had gone, no one knew whither.

But there were those who could not and would not believe it of him, and foremost among them was the minister.   The evidence against him was mainly circumstantial ; the principal accuser was Frost, and the chain of circumstances that linked Graham with the crime were substantially as follows :

The boy who worked around the mill-house and slept in the second story of the Graham's cottage testified that about half an hour before sunset Sunday evening he heard old Morrow "cussing and swearing" at somebody down in the mill, while he was going out to drive the cows home ; didn't see who it was, but ten minutes afterwards as he came back he saw Graham pitching stones into the stream down below the mill, "looking queer ;" called to him twice, but Graham did not answer ; supposed he was mad at the old man for cussing him so—they had had lots of trouble for a week ; heard the old man tell him he was going to get rid of him if he didn't do different.

That night he (the witness) went out in the country a piece and did not come home until half-past ten. It was all dark around the mill when he got back.   It had been raining, but the sky was brighter then, and as he passed the south door he was surprised to see it open. The old man generally locked it and went home early. He was just going to go and shut it when a man came out. It "skeered" him because the old man had given him fits for being out late and lying abed in the morning, so he stopped short to wait until he got away. The man shut and locked the door, and walked up the road ahead of him, and then he saw that it was not the old man, but young Graham, and that Mr. Graham was going straight up to the mill-house, so he cut across to the cottage and got in soft as he could. Yes, it might have been eleven o'clock by that time, and he did not want Mr. Frost, or Mr. Graham either, to know he was out so late. It was all dark at the mill-house, and all dark at the cottage, but Mr. Frost heard him and called him into his room and asked for a dipper of water. Mr. Frost was in bed and asked him what time it was, and said he had been asleep, but waked up with a headache; told him he did not know the time; didn't want him to know it was so late, 'cause he might tell the old man. Mr. Frost asked him where Dick was, and just then they heard Dick coming up the front steps, and the witness went up to his own room. Heard them talking down-stairs for a little while, but could not understand what they were saying; did not listen particularly; went to sleep, and slept a good while; was awakened by hearing some noise in Dick's room, which was directly under his—sounded like something glass being broken, but everything was quiet right off, and he thought he might have dreamed it. Next thing he knowed it was morning, and Mandy, the cook over at the mill-house, was calling to him from the bottom of the stairs to get up right off—the master hadn't come home all night, and there was people waitin' down at the mill. Dick's room was open and the bed hadn't been slept on, and his clothes and things were all thrown all round on the floor ; it looked queer, she said ; he was gone, too ; ran down as quick as he could dress and called Mr. Frost, who was asleep in bed and did not wake easy ; called him three or four times and banged on the door, and at last opened it and called him louder ; then he woke up slowly and wanted to know the matter ; told him Mandy said Mr. Morrow had not been home and that Dick was not there, and there was farmers with wheat at the mill. He said go and open the mill and he would be down in a minute ; told him that Dick had the key and had locked the mill late last night ; saw him do it. Mr. Frost jumped right up in bed excited like and said, " You saw him do it ! When, where were you ?" and so had to tell him about Dick's being there, coming out of the mill late as nearly eleven o'clock. Then Mandy came back and said she found the key hanging on the peg inside the hall-door, and witness took it and went down and opened the south door. The office window-shade was down and the office door on the east side was shut, and so it was kinder dark, but he and the two men waiting there went right through the mill into the office, and there they found the old man dead on the floor, with lots of blood streaming

16

from his head. It skeered him awful, and they ran out. Then Mr. Frost came, and he was pale, and said, "My God, what an awful thing !" and they sent right to 'Mahbin for Dr. Green, and the mayor and constable ; and that was all he knowed.

Doctor Green's testimony, divested of professional technicalities, was to the effect that the miller had been killed at least six or eight hours, and that death was the result of the gun-shot wound through the head. The bullet was found imbedded in the skull at the back of the head, and had entered under the left eye. The face was burned and blackened by powder. No other wound or hurt was found upon the body. The doctor had arrived at the mill about 6.45 A.M., accompanied by Mr. Lowrie, the mayor of Nemahbin, an old friend of the deceased. When they arrived, Mr. Frost was in charge of the premises, and stated that no one had entered the office since the moment he had arrived at the spot.

Mr. Lowrie testified to coming with the doctor ; being received by Mr. Frost and ushered into the office. The deceased was then lying on his face with his feet near the window. There was much blood on the floor, and spattered on the legs of an office chair that stood close by the head. No weapon of any kind was found in the office, and the object of the murder was explained at a glance ; the desk was rifled, the safe was open, and while the papers therein were found undisturbed, the cash drawer, in which it was known that the deceased generally kept a good deal of money, was empty. Other testimony established the fact that

he had as much as five hundred dollars in the drawer
on the previous Saturday. In presence of the mayor,
constable, Mr. Frost, and one or two neighbors, the
bullet had been cut out from behind by the doctor.
It was slightly flattened, and in shape, and in its exact weight as subsequently determined, it corresponded
exactly with those of a "five-shooting" revolver of
peculiar make known as "the Avenger." To Mr.
Lowrie's knowledge only two pistols of that kind were
owned in that neighborhood, and both had been bought
by him two years before at a time when there was a
scare about mad dogs. One he still owned, and it
was now at home, locked up in his desk ; the other
was Richard Graham's, and he had seen it in his possession less than a week ago.

Mr. Frost's testimony, given with much emotion
and apparent reluctance, was to this effect : His first
knowledge of the murder was Monday morning about
six o'clock, when summoned to the mill by the tidings
that Mr. Morrow had not been home all night. Going
to the east entrance, he found the boy, Schaffer, and
two young farmers, frightened and excited over what
they had seen in the office. He went in at once, followed by them, and saw at a glance that murder had
been done, though his first thought was suicide. He
merely turned the body enough to see that the wound
was in the face, and to satisfy himself and the others
that no pistol was near, and then, pointing to the fact
that the safe and desk were both open, he ordered
everybody out and closed the door until the arrival
of the officials from Nemahbin.

Questioned as to his own movements the previous night, he said that after supper, when Graham drove the ladies to town, he himself had gone home and read an hour, but, feeling drowsy, had gone to bed, waking up some hours later with a headache on hearing the boy coming in. The boy said he didn't know the time, but it must have been eleven o'clock, and just then Graham came up the steps and the boy went to his own room; witness called out to him twice and got no answer, and at last, thinking it queer that Graham did not go to bed, but kept moving briskly about, he rose and went into the front room in his night-shirt, and found Graham packing a big satchel he had, and rummaging through the clothes on the pegs. Asked him what was the matter, and Graham hardly noticed him—merely said he was going away awhile; could not help noticing how queer and strange he looked, and how oddly he behaved; he was very pale, and muttered to himself every now and then; asked him twice if he had any reason for going, and when he would return, but only got evasive answers and averted looks; knew that there had been ugly words between the deceased and Graham very often during the month past, and that there was an angry altercation between them down at the mill just before supper-time; the deceased had told him tha., he was going to discharge Graham; he was getting too insolent and rebellious to suit him; Graham hardly ate anything at supper, and the old man did not come up to the house until after they had driven off to church. That was the last he saw of him alive—as he passed the cottage on

his way to the mill-house.   Asked as to whether anything of unusual or suspicious nature had occurred
during the day or evening, Frost said that one thing
struck him as queer.   Graham's revolver hung habitu-
ally at the head of his bed, and when he concluded to
go to bed that evening he went into Graham's room
to look at the clock and saw that his pistol was gone.
It had been there during the day, and he never knew
him to carry it before.   Asked if he saw it in Graham's possession Sunday night, he replied that he saw
it sticking from the hip pocket of his trousers ; that
Graham had his coat off and was washing his hands
at the time.   One other ugly circumstance was noted :
Graham had been burning a lot of papers and things
in the stove before being interrupted.   When the
stove was examined in the morning some buttons were
found, charred and partially destroyed in the ashes,
but they were clearly identified as the buttons of the
canvas overalls Graham wore around the mill—which
were missing—and behind the stove was found a fine
cambric handkerchief that Graham only used when
he wore his best, or Sunday suit, which he had on all
that day, and this handkerchief was stained with blood.

Nellie Morrow was so fearfully agitated by the
tragedy that her own evidence was only drawn from
her bit by bit.   She confirmed the statement of Dick's
pallor and his silence all that evening, and then with
hysterical sobbing told of their quarrel after church
and his leaving her, as he said, never to return ; but
she protested that he had "never a thing against
father," and that he never, never could have harmed

him.   All other obtainable evidence had the same
general tendency, and despite his years of sturdy pro-
bity and the excellence of his character, Dick Graham
had to bear the burden of the accumulation of evidence against him.   The absent always have the worst
of it, and his flight had confirmed the theories of many
an unwilling mind.   He was the murderer of his former
friend and benefactor.

<hr>

CHAPTER IV.

A WEEK passed, and with no tidings of him.   Detectives had been scouring the country in every direction.   A man answering his description was arrested
in Chicago, and turned out to be somebody else.   A
dozen times it was reported that now the sleuth-
hounds of the law had run down their victim, but
the entire month of July passed away, and the community had gradually settled down to the belief that
Graham had made good his escape and taken with
him some five hundred dollars of his murdered master's money.

Old Morrow had been duly and reverently buried.
A younger brother from a distant state came to the
scene as executor of the will, in conjunction with Mr.
Lowrie, and under his management the mill resumed
its functions for the benefit of the estate.   Except
some legacies to this brother and to the sister who
had taken charge of Nellie and his household, old
Morrow had left his property, valued at over forty

thousand dollars, to be divided equally between his two children should Sam reappear; but if proof of his death were obtained, his share was to go to Nellie.

A week after the funeral, acting on the advice of the minister and the village doctor, Nellie's relatives sent her to Chicago. She had suffered greatly in health, and was in a condition of nervous depression. Whenever Dick's crime was mentioned in her presence, she would vehemently assert her belief in his innocence, and then shudderingly accuse herself, with piteous crying, of being the cause of all his trouble, and perhaps of her father's death. Another thing. She who had plainly shown herself fascinated by Mr. Frost's many graces and attractions during the preceding winter, now refused to see him. He hung around the house, full of respectful sympathy and lover-like interest, but was visibly chagrined at her persistent avoidance. To the minister she confessed that she had been greatly interested in Frost—perhaps a little in love with him; he flattered and delighted her, and it made Dick jealous. She didn't know how or why she so encouraged him, but she had, and now she shrank from seeing him at all. Her deep affliction would excuse it.

A week after she left for Chicago Mr. Frost concluded that he would go thither himself. The new master needed no bookkeeper, he said, and Frost was too fine a gentleman to do Dick's work around the mill. He was neither invited to go nor to stay. He was allowed to go and come without apparent let or hindrance, yet, before the train which bore him away was well out of sight, a new farm-hand, who worked at odd jobs around a neighboring place on the lake, suddenly entered the railway station, wrote ten hurried words on a telegraph-blank, and handed it to the operator, whereupon the operator gazed at him in quick surprise, then whistled softly to himself, nodded appreciatively, and clicked away the message, with the addition of a cabalistic " Rush," and Mr. Frost's train was boarded at Milwaukee by a number of people who took no special note of him, and by one man who never lost sight of him from that moment until he locked his bedroom door behind him at night.

Then the minister received a call from the new farm-hand, who brought with him a young man who worked on a place over near Eagle Prairie, a railway station some distance off to the southwest. This young man had spent Sunday calling on a sweetheart in 'Mahbin, and had started about 7.30 P.M. to walk to the large town seven miles away, where he would take the cars homeward. He saw Nellie, her aunt, and a young man driving into town, and by eight o'clock he himself was passing the mill. It was just growing dark, so that he could not distinguish faces, but he saw two men standing by the office—one short, stout, and elderly, the other tall and slender and straight. The older man was talking furiously and angrily ; heard him say, " I told you an hour ago to keep away from me. You have lied to me right along. You are a thief and a scoundrel, I believe, and you are a damned coward and deserter—a deserter, by God ! and I've got the papers to prove it !"

What the tall man said he could not hear. He spoke low—seemed to be arguing with the old man, begging him to be quiet, and they went into the office. Then the young man walked on a few hundred yards, when it came on to rain very hard, and he stopped and took shelter under a little fishing-shed there was right at the edge of the lake. The rain held up in fifteen minutes, and he started on again over the causeway, "and hadn't more'n got a rod" when he heard what sounded like a pistol-shot back at the mill. He stopped short and listened two minutes, but heard nothing more, so went on and thought no more of it until he heard of the murder—but that was not until a week after it happened, when he came up from the farm to Eagle village and heard people talking about it.

But with the first week in August came exciting news. Far to the northwest across the Missouri, Dick Graham had been traced and followed by a Wisconsin detective, who found him in the uniform of the regular army, just marching off with his comrades to join General Terry's forces, then in the field up the Yellowstone. In his possession was the Avenger revolver and over one hundred dollars in greenbacks. On two five-dollar bills there was a broad and ugly stain, which microscopic examination proved to be blood. Graham appeared utterly stunned at the arrest; expressed the greatest grief and horror at hearing of the murder of Mr. Morrow, and professed his entire willingness to go back and stand trial. The story of i is "escape" to that distance was now easily told. The detectives had speedily satisfied themselves he had got away on none of the regular trains that week, but one bright fellow had learned that four cars full of troops had passed west late that Sunday night, and followed the clue. They had gone through to Bismarck—a tedious journey in '76—and thither he followed. Thence the troops had gone by boat up the Missouri, and he took the first opportunity that came —and the next boat going up. At Fort Buford he "sighted" his man, told his story to the commanding officer of the post, who sent for the officers of the troops with whom poor Dick was serving. They promptly asserted that their first knowledge of him was on the Monday they reached St. Paul, when a sergeant brought him to them, saying he begged to be allowed to enlist and go with them. He told a perfectly straight story ; said he was an orphan, unmarried, had been a miller, but was tired of small wages, hard work, and no hopes of getting ahead, and had made up his mind to get into the regulars. Was at the railway station at midnight when the train was side-tracked to allow another to pass, and appealed to the sergeant of the guard to take him along ; said he would pay his way until they could enlist him, and as he was a likely fellow they were glad to have him. He had won everybody's respect in the short time he was with them, and the whole command seemed thunderstruck to hear of the allegations against him.

The detective and his prisoner were put on a boat going back to Bismarck, and on that same boat, returning, wounded and furloughed, was a sergeant of the Seventh Cavalry—a gallant fellow who had fought under Benteen and McDougall on the bluffs of the Little Horn, after Custer's command had been surrounded and slaughtered four miles farther down stream. The sergeant kept to his room and bunk until they got to Bismarck, but the detectives had a chance to see and talk with him—and so had Graham.

It was an eventful day when the detective and his prisoner reached Nemahbin. The minister was there to meet him, as was Mr. Lowrie, and the entire male population of the neighborhood. There was no disorder or turbulence. Dick was quietly escorted to a room in the constable's house—they had no jail—and there that night he had a long conference with the minister and other prominent citizens. The minister drove home quite late—but very much later, along towards two in the morning, in fact, he was at the railway station and received in his buggy the single passenger who alighted from the night express.

Next day there was a gathering at the mayor's office—an apartment in the municipal residence devoted to dining-room duty three times a day, and opening into the kitchen on the one hand, into the hallway on another, and into the village post-office on the third. Here sat Mr. Lowrie, the doctor, the constable, other local celebrities, and one or two distinguished importations from Milwaukee. Here was the minister, looking singularly wide-awake, lively, and brisk for a man who had been up all night; here, too, sat the farmhand who sent the cabalistic despatch when Frost went to Chicago, and the young man who heard the conversation down at the mill that Sunday night;

here, too, sat Dick, looking pale but tranquil, and
hither, too, presently came Mr. Frost, looking ghastly
pale and very far from tranquil. Dick looked squarely at him as he entered, but Frost glanced rapidly
about the room, eagerly nodding to one man after another, but avoiding Dick entirely. Then followed an
impressive silence.

Outside, the August sun was streaming hotly down
upon the heads of an intensely curious and interested
throng ; inside there was for the moment no sound
but the humming of a thousand flies, or the nervous
scraping of a boot over the uncarpeted floor. Then
the mayor whispered a few words to the minister,
who nodded to Mr. Morrow, the surviving brother,
and then Mr. Morrow stepped into the hallway leading to the mayor's parlor, and presently reappeared at
the doorway, and quietly said, "All right."

All eyes turned to glance at him at this moment,
but, beyond his square, squat figure, nothing in the
darkened hallway was visible. Then the mayor cleared
his throat and began :

" By the consent of the proper authorities the prisoner, accused of the murder of the late Samuel Morrow, has been brought here instead of to the county
town, for reasons that will appear hereafter. Graham,
you have desired to hear the evidence of Mr. Frost,
one of the principal witnesses against you at the time
of the discovery of the murder. The clerk will now
read it."

And read it the clerk did, in monotonous singsong.
Graham sat clinching his fists and his teeth, and look-

ing straight at Frost as the reading was finished. The latter, uneasily shifting in his chair, still looked anywhere else around the room.

"Do you wish to say anything, Graham?" asked the mayor, in answer to the appeal in Dick's eyes.

"I do, sir. That statement is a lie almost from beginning to end. I had no quarrel, no words with Mr. Morrow that Sunday evening—never spoke to him at all. It was Frost himself who was with him at the mill before supper. As to the rest of the evening I know nothing of what happened. When I got home, and put up the horse and buggy, it must have been long after ten. Then I found the east door of the mill was open, and went in and found everything dark and quiet; came out and locked the door (but never went into the office), and took the key up to the millhouse, and hung it up on the hook in the hall. I supposed Mr. Morrow was asleep in bed. Then I went home and burned some old letters and papers and packed some things in my bag. I was going away for good—I've told the doctor and the minister why —they know well enough—and I called Frost; he owed me twenty dollars, and I needed it, and woke him up, if he was asleep, and asked him for it, and the very money he gave me was in those five-dollar bills. I never burned my overalls. I *did* lose my handkerchief somewhere about the house that night, and never missed it until I was gone; and I never had my revolver until just before I took my bag and started, and never knew until days afterwards—way up the Northern Pacific—that one of the chambers was emptied. As for the murder, I never heard of it until I was arrested."

"Mr. Frost," said the mayor, "you made no mention in your evidence of paying money to the prisoner."

"Certainly not," said Frost, promptly, but his eyes glittered, and his face was white as a sheet. "Nothing of the kind happened. That money came direct from the mill safe."

"How do you know?"

"Well—of course—I don't know that; but it is my belief."

"Mr. Frost, there was no mention in your testimony of a violent altercation between yourself and the late Mr. Morrow at the mill that evening after Graham came in town with the ladies. Why did you omit that?"

He was livid now, and the strong, white hands were twitching nervously. All eyes were fastened upon him as he stood confronting the mayor, his back towards the hallway, where, in grim silence, stood Mr. Morrow.

"I know of no such altercation," he stammered.

"Were you ever accused of being a deserter from the army?"

Every one saw the nervous start he gave, but, though haggard and wild, he stuck to his false colors.

"Never, sir."

"That's a lie," said a deep voice out in the hall, and at the unconventional interruption there was a general stir. Men leaned forward and craned their

necks to peer behind Mr. Morrow, who stood there
immovable.

"Order, gentlemen, if you please," said Mr. Lowrie.

"Then how and where did you know Sam Morrow,
as you convinced his father you did?"

"I?—out in Arizona, where I was mining."

"Why did you not fulfil your promise, as you said
you could and would?"

"I couldn't. That was what made the old man
down on me. I did believe last winter I could find
Sam and get him home, but I could not bear to tell
the old man he was killed with General Custer."

"That's another lie!" came from the hallway, and,
brushing past Mr. Morrow's squat figure, there strode
into the room a tall, bronzed-faced, soldierly fellow in
the undress uniform of a sergeant of cavalry.

Men sprang to their feet and fairly shouted. Old
Doctor Green threw his arms about the soldier's neck
in the excess of his joy. There was a rush forward
from the post-office doorway to greet him, a cry of
"Sam Morrow!" and then another cry—a yell—a
scurry and crash at the kitchen entrance. "Quick!
Head him off! Catch him!" were the cries, and then
came a dash into the open air.

With a spring like that of a panther Frost had
leaped into the unguarded kitchen, thence to the fence
beyond, and now was running like a deer through the
quiet village street towards the railway. A hundred
men were in pursuit in a moment, and in that open
country there was no shelter for skulking criminal, no
lair in which he could hide till night. In half an

hour, exhausted, half dead with terror and despair, the wretched man was dragged back, and now, limp and dejected, cowered in the presence of his accusers.

CHAPTER V.

SAM MORROW told his story in a few words. He had served in the Seventh Cavalry for five years under the name of Samuel Moore, and two years before, while with his troop on the Yellowstone, the man calling himself Frost was a sergeant in another company. He was only a short time in the regiment, but his fine appearance, intelligence, and education led to his speedy appointment as sergeant, and as Sergeant Farrand he had been for a few months a popular and respected man; but as soon as they got back to winter-quarters he turned out to be a gambler, then a swindler and card-sharper. He lost the respect of both officers and men, got into a gambling-scrape with some teamsters in Bismarck, was locked up by the civil authorities, and, after a series of troubles of that description, deserted the service in the Black Hills the summer of '75, taking three horses with him, and that was the last seen of him until now. Sam had been shot in the arm in the fight of the 25th of June, after the Indians had butchered Custer's part of the regiment, and now, having served out his time, was once more home, with an honorable discharge and a certificate of high character from his officers.

In substantiation of Sam's story, Mr. Morrow exhibited two letters which he had found among his brother's papers. They were from the adjutant of the Seventh Cavalry, in reply, evidently, to inquiries which old Morrow had instituted in May, and the second one contained a description of Frost as the soldier Farrand, which tallied exactly.

"And now, Frost, what have you to say as to the murder?" was the next question; and, cowering and abject, the wretch sat with bowed head and trembling limbs, gasping, "I did not do it, I did not do it." But this Nemahbin would believe no longer. There was a wild cry of "Hang him!" from the excited crowd in the street, and then came a scene. Peaceful and law-abiding as had been the community, it turned in almost savage fury upon the scoundrel who had sought to charge his own crime upon an innocent and long-respected citizen. A dozen resolute men leaped through the post-office to the doorway of the inner room, but there they halted. Between them and the cowering form of Frost stood the tall figure of Sam Morrow, his eyes ablaze, his mouth set and stern, his left arm in a sling, but in his right hand a levelled revolver.

"Back, every man of you!" he said. "He killed my father, but, by God, it has got to be a fair trial!" Lowrie, the doctor, and the detective were at his back, and Nemahbin hesitated, thought better of its mad impulse, and retired. That night Frost lay behind the prison bars, accused of an array of crimes, with cold-blooded murder as the climax, and Sam Morrow, Dick Graham, and Nellie met once more at the old home.

17

In less than a month Frost's last hope had gone. Whether his pluck and nerve had given out entirely, whether the rapid accumulation of damaging evidence had made him fearful that even hanging would be too good for him if all his past were "ferreted out," as now seemed likely, or whether he hoped, by confession, to gain mercy, is not known; but, before his trial, he made full admission of his guilt. He had come to Nemahbin hoping to get such a hold on the old man by telling him he could find Sam that he would be welcomed, and allowed to prosecute his suit with Nellie, who was plainly fascinated. If he could gain her love and her hand, he might settle down, be respectable on old Morrow's money, and then, even if Sam did come home, he would not be apt to expose the man his sister loved and married. But his efforts to convince the old man that he was trying to find Sam, while all the time he was doing all he knew how to keep him on the wrong track, were at constant cross-purposes. The old man soon became suspicious of him, would advance him no money, paid him a nominal sum for keeping books, etc., the first three months he was there, then relieved him of that duty, and kept up incessant cross-questioning. At last Frost found out that Graham suspected him of being a deserter, and that the old man had got that idea and also that his own boy was somewhere in the army. Then came the news of the Custer massacre, and by that time he felt sure he could win Nellie's hand if her father's consent could be gained; but Morrow was all suspicion and eagerness, and Frost knew by his manner that he was on the trail of his lost boy by means of letters—and these letters would plainly betray him, who had deserted from Sam's own regiment. He hurried to Chicago, and there—there he came upon that list of killed in the battle of the Little Big Horn, and among the names was the one he wanted to see, Sergeant Sam Moore. It decided him at once. He went to his uncle, claiming that he was about to marry Nellie Morrow, got from him a small supply of money, and came back determined to win her at once. She was the old man's only child and sole heir. That very day Morrow had told him that he had found him out, that in his absence he had received letters proving him to b⌐ a scoundrel, and, giving him just one chance to tell him where his lost boy was or to leave. Frost feared to tell then, as he knew the miller would insist on proofs, and in some way his own connection with the regiment would be known. That evening, before tea, Morrow, in an angry interview, which Schaffer partially overheard, told him he had proofs of his rascality—letters to settle his case for good and all. Then he became desperate. Soon as Dick had gone to town with the ladies he went to Graham's room, got the revolver, and once more went to the mill, and found Morrow at the office door. It was then almost dark. Then came the accusation of desertion, and, once in the office, Morrow had called him by his soldier name, and Frost knew "all was up." He must have those papers. He drew the revolver to frighten the old man, and it went off, killing him instantly. He was horror-stricken, but strove

to collect himself. Flight would betray him at once
as the murderer. Why not make it a case of suicide
—leave the pistol by him? No — that would not
do. It was Graham's— Ha! why not make Graham the guilty one? Quickly he got the safe key
from the old man's pocket, unlocked and obtained the
cash-drawer, with its five hundred dollars in greenbacks—opened the desk, and rummaged through the
letters till he found one from the headquarters of the
Seventh Cavalry, which gave a description of several
men almost his height and general appearance who
had deserted. Among them he recognized his own
and his soldier name. With these he went to the cottage, leaving all dark at the mill, burned the letter,
hid portions of the money in Graham's mattress, and
was thinking, in terror, what to do next, when he heard
voices on the road. He dare not go out, and so wasted
some time in the house. When he heard Graham drive
back with the buggy he hurriedly undressed and went
to bed. Then Schaffer came home and he called him
in, that the boy might say that he was in bed and undressed; but when Graham entered he shammed sleep.
Roused, at last, by Graham's demand for his money
and the news that he was going away, an idea occurred
to him. Cutting a slit in his finger with a razor, he let
the blood fall on a couple of five-dollar bills—smeared
and quickly dried it—gave them to Graham before he
started, and as soon as he was gone went busily to
work. Going down to the mill as soon as satisfied
that all was safe—Schaffer asleep and Dick far on his
way to the railroad—he found the east door locked.

Then he knew that Graham had been there; had locked the door and taken the key to the hall of the mill-house, and of course had seen nothing of the body. He got the key, obtained Graham's overalls from the mill, burned them in the stove at the cottage—as he argued Dick could have done had he bloodied them in the affray—and then in Graham's room had found his cambric handkerchief. Once more he went down to the ghostly mill, and dipped this into the blood of his victim; then locked the mill door (he had locked the office door, leaving the key inside), put the key back in the house, returned to the cottage, and to bed. He had woven a chain for Graham that, added to the poor fellow's flight and his previous disagreements, would fasten all suspicion on him as the murderer. Then he thought of the money. He rose, bundled it loosely in an old oyster-can, stole out in the gray light of approaching dawn, and buried it in the loose sand down on the shore of the mill-pond, just where all the cattle would go for water, and trample out all traces within an hour; then once more he went back to bed, and to the counterfeited sleep from which Schaffer had such difficulty in rousing him. It was well planned—and when he heard the boy declare he had seen Graham coming from the mill at 11 o'clock he thought it perfect.

But he had failed to cross one track—the bloody print of a slender, city-made, shapely boot on the flour-dusted floor under the peg where Graham's overalls generally hung. It was the only footprint in that corner of the old mill, and Frost's was the only boot in all Nemahbin that would fit it. Keen eyes had noted this even while the wiseacres of the law were urging the pursuit of Graham; and then came the inexorable watch on every move that Frost might make. Even without his confession, the relentless search of the detectives would have run him down. And now Dick Graham was free.

It wasn't such a mystery, after all. A greater one was being enacted right here in the old mill-house, whither Nellie had hurriedly returned on the telegraphic news of Sam's home-coming. She had sent Dick Graham sorrowing to his fate only a month ago. She never wished to see him or speak to him again. She had twined her girlish hero-worship around the tall beauty of Mr. Frost, and seen it shrivel with aversion in a single day. And now, surrounded by the halo of his sufferings, his self-imposed exile, his years of patient, uncomplaining, unswerving devotion, here was her brother's best friend, sharing with that brother the admiration and homage of their little village circle; here was her true lover, Dick, loving, forgiving, unreproaching, and yet unseeking, and one sweet August night, calm and still and starlit, she stood at the very gate where he had seen her parting with Frost that dread Sunday morning. And now her little hand was trembling on his arm as he would have closed the gate behind him. He felt the detaining pressure, and turned, gently as ever:

"What is it, Nellie?"

"Dick, will you never forgive me for what I said—that night?"

One instant he could hardly speak—hardly breathe; but then, slowly, with swimming eyes and quivering lips, soft and tremulous, she looked up into his radiant face.

And now—eight years after—'Mahbin Mill hums and whirs more merrily than ever.   Dick Graham is master and manager, for Sam, with a well-earned strap of gold-lace on each broad shoulder, has gone back to the frontier life he learned to love in the old regiment. Frost languished but a few months in his prison before death mercifully took him away, and Nellie—Nellie is the happiest little woman around Nemahbin for miles; only those two scamps, Sam and Dick, seven and five years old respectively, keep her in a fidget and their father in a chuckle with their pranks.   They are always in mischief or the mill-pond.

PLODDER'S PROMOTION.

For five years the life of Second Lieutenant Plodder, of the —th Foot, had been a burden to him. For more than five years Second Lieutenant Plodder had been something of a burden to the —th Foot. In the dreary monotone in which the psalm of life is sung, or was sung, in frontier garrisons before the introduction of such wildly diverting exercises as daily target practice, or measuring-distance drill, the one thing that became universally detestable was the man with the perennial grievance, and Mr. Plodder's grievance was slow promotion. There was nothing exceptionally harrowing in his individual experience; dozens of other fellows in his own and in other regiments were victims of the same malady, but for some reason Mr. Plodder considered himself the especial target of the slings and arrows of a fortune too outrageous for even a downtrodden "dough-boy" to bear in silence, and the dreary burden of his song—morn, noon, and night—was the number of years he had served, and might yet have to serve, with never a bar to his strap of faded blue.

Entering the army as a volunteer in '61, he had emerged, after four years of singularly uneventful soldiering, a lieutenant in the company in which he

started as private. Provost-guard duty and the like
had told but little on the aggregate of present for
duty with his command, and that sort of campaigning being congenial, Mr. Plodder concluded to keep
it up as a profession. A congressional friend got
him a second-lieutenancy at the close of the war,
and the devil himself, said Mr. Plodder, got him into
that particular regiment. "I never saw such a God-
forsaken lot of healthy fellers in my life," he was
wont to declare over the second or third toddy at
"the store" in the long wintry evenings. "There
ain't a man of 'em died in six years, and here I am
after nigh onto twelve years' consecutive service, and
I ain't a first lieutenant yit."

We youngsters, with our light hearts and lighter
pockets, used to rather enjoy getting old Plodder
started, it must be confessed; and when pin-pool or
auction-pitch had palled in interest, and we would be
casting about for some time-killing device, and the
word would come from the window, scattering the
group of oldsters, that Plodder was on his way to the
store, somebody would be apt to suggest a project for
"putting up a job on Grumpy," and it would be carried *nem. con.*

"Heard the news, Plod?" some young reprobate
would carelessly inquire while banging the balls about
the table.

"What news?" says Plodder.

"You're in for a file. They say old Cramps is
going to die. He's off on leave now."

"Who says so?" says Plodder, eying his interloc-

utor askance. He is always suspicious of the youngsters.

"Fact, Plodder. Ask the major, if you don't believe me."

And before long Plodder would be sure to make
his way into the inner court—the *sanctum sanctorum*
of the store—sacred ordinarily to the knot of old officers who liked to have their quiet game aloof from
the crash of pool-pins and the babel of voices in the
main room, and there, after more or less beating round
the bush, he would inquire as to whether the major
had recently heard news of old Captain Cramps, and
what was the state of his health; returning then to
the billiard-room with wrath and vengeance in his
eye, to upbraid his tormentor for sending him off on
such a cruel quest.

"Well, what did you go for?" would be the extent
of his comfort. "I only said Cramps was going to
die, and it's my profound conviction he will—some
time or other."

And Plodder would groan in spirit, "It's all very
well for you youngsters, but just you wait till you've
served as long as I have, twelve years' consecutive
service, by George! and if you don't wish lineal promotion would come in, or the grass was growing green
over every man that ever opposed it, you can stop *my*
pay."

It got to be a serious matter at last. It was Plod's
monomania. We used to swear that Plod spent half
his time moaning over the army register, and that his
eyes were never fixed upon the benevolent features

of his captain but that he was wondering whether apoplexy would not soon give him the longed-for file. Every week or two there would come tidings of deaths, dismissals, resignations, or retirements in some other corps or regiment, and second lieutenant so-or-so would become first lieutenant *vice* somebody else, and on such occasions poor old Plod would suffer the tortures of the damned. "There's that boy," he would say, "only two years out of that national charity school up there on the Hudson, in leading-strings, by George! when we fellers were fightin' and bleedin' an—"

"Hello, Plod! I forgot you fought and bled in the provost-guard. Where was it, old man? Take a nip and tell us about it," some one would interpose, but Plodder would plunge ahead in the wild recitative of his lament, and the floor would be his own.

Tuesday evenings always found him at the store. The post-trader's copy of the *Army and Navy Journal* arrived soon after retreat, and it was one of the unwritten laws of the establishment that old Plod should have first glimpse. There had been a time when he resorted to the quarters of brother-officers and possessed himself of their copy, but his concomitant custom of staying two or three hours and bemoaning his luck had gradually been the means of barring him out, and never having a copy of his own (for Plodder was thrifty and "near"), he had settled into the usurpation of first rights with "Mr. O'Bottle's" paper, and there at the store he devoured the column of casualties with disappointed eyes, and swallowed grief and toddy in "consecutive" gulps.

It used to be asserted of Plodder that he was fig-
uring for the Signal Corps.   He was at one time generally known as "Old Probabilities;" indeed, it had
been his nickname for several years.   He was accused
of keeping a regular system of "indications" against
the names of his seniors in rank, and that godless
young reprobate Trickett so far forgot his reverence
for rank as to prepare and put in circulation "Plodder's Probabilities," a Signal Service burlesque that
had the double effect of alienating that gentleman's
long-tried friendship and startling into unnatural blas-
phemy the staid captains who figured in the bulletin.
Something in this wise it ran (and though poor fun
at best, was better than anything we had had since
that wonderful day when "Mrs. *Captain* O'Rorke av
ye plaze" dropped that letter addressed to her friend
"Mrs. Captain Sullivan, O'Maher Barrix") :

"PLODDER'S PROBABILITIES.

" *For Captain Irvin.*—Higher living together with lower ex-
ercise.   Cloudy complexion, with temperament choleric veer-
ing to apoplectic.   Impaired action followed by fatty degen-
eration of the heart.

" *For Captains Prime and Chipsey.*—Barometer threatening.
Squalls domestic.   Stocks lower.   Putler and Soaker bills falling (due N.E., S., and W.) from all parts of the country.

" *For Lieutenant Cole, R. Q. M.*—Heft increasing.   Nose and
eyelids turgid.   Frequent (d)rains, Sp. Fru.   Heavy shortage
C. and G. E., S. T. 187(—)X.

"*Cautionary Signals* for Burroughs, Calvin, and Waterman.
Something sure to turn up."

We were hard up for fun in those days, and even

this low order of wit excited a high degree of hilarity.   The maddest men were Prime, Chipsey, and the
R.Q.M., but their wrath was as nothing compared with
the blaze of indignation which illuminated the coun-
tenances of Mrs. Prime and Mrs. Chipsey, next-door
neighbors and bosom friends as feminine friendships
go.   Each lady in this instance was ready to acknowledge the pertinence of Mr. Trickett's diagnosis in the
case of her neighbor's husband, and confidentially to
admit that there was even some justification for the
allegation of "squalls domestic" next door, but that
anything of this sort should be even hinted at in her
own case, nothing but utter moral depravity on the
part of the perpetrator could account for it.   Trickett
paid dear for his whistle, but for the time it seemed
to hold Plodder in check.   The ruling passion soon
cropped out again, however.   Gray hairs were beginning to sprinkle his scanty beard, and crow's-feet to
grow more deeply under his suspicious eyes.   He never
looked at a senior without a semi-professional scrutiny
of that senior's physical condition as set forth in the
clearness of his eye or skin.   He never shook hands
without conveying the impression that he was reaching for a man's pulse.   If any old officer were mentioned as going off on "surgeon's certificate" to visit
the sea-shore, and the question should be asked,
"What's the matter with him?" the interrogated
party invariably responded, "Don't know.   Ask Plodder."

It was not only in the regiment that Plodder became
a notoriety.   For one eventful year of its history the

—th Foot was stationed in close proximity to department headquarters, and department headquarters became speedily and intimately acquainted with Mr. Plodder. Having once made his calls of ceremony upon the commanding general and his staff, it became his custom to make frequent visits to the city, and, passing beyond the established haunts where his comrades were wont to dispense for creature comforts their scanty dimes, to spend some hours pottering about the offices at headquarters. But for a month no one really fathomed the object of his attentions. "Trying to get a soft detail in town" was the theory hazarded by some of the youngsters, who were well aware of his distaste for company duty; "Boning for aide-de-camp," suggested another. But not until the medical director one day explosively alluded to him as "that —— old vampire-bat," with an uncomplimentary and profane adjective in place of the ——, and the acting judge-advocate of the department impulsively asked if "that infernal Mark Meddle couldn't be kept at home," did it begin to dawn on us what old Plodder really was driving at. His theory being that army casualties could be divided up pretty evenly between the Medical Department and the Bureau of Military Justice as the expediting means, he hoped by ingenious engineering of the conversation to pick up points as to probabilities in the —th Foot, or to furnish such as might be lacking.

In plain words, it transpired about this time that Plodder had taken to haunting the office of the judge-advocate at hours when he could hope for uninter-

18

rupted conversation with that officer, and one day, with very ruffled demeanor, he was encountered making hurried exit therefrom, pursued, said Mr. Trickett, by the toe of the judge-advocate's boot. Indeed, Mr. Trickett was not far wrong. He and his now reconciled captain were about calling upon the judge-advocate when Plodder burst forth, and surely there was every symptom of a wrathful intent in the attitude of the staff-officer whom they met at the door. It was a minute or so before he could recover his composure, though he politely invited them to enter and be seated. No explanation was vouchsafed as to what had occurred, but Trickett and Prime came back to barracks full of speculation and curiosity, told pretty much everybody what they had seen, and, all being convinced that Plodder and the judge-advocate had had some kind of a row, it was determined to draw Plodder out. Consequently there was a gathering in the billiard-room that night, and when Plodder entered, with visage of unusual gloom, he ought to have been put on his guard by the unexpectedly prompt and cheery invites to "take something" that greeted him. But Plodder had been taking several somethings in the privacy of his quarters, and, being always ready to partake at somebody else's expense, he was speedily primed into talkative mood, and then the inquisition began.

"Saw you coming out of Park's office to-day," said Prime. "What was your hurry?"

No answer for a moment, then a rather sulky growl, "I'd finished my business, and thought you might want to see him."

"I? Lord, no! What should I want to see him for except socially?"

No answer.

"*Nice* fellow, Park," said Trickett; "seems such a calm, self-poised sort of man, you know."

"One of the most courteous men I ever met," said Waterman.

Then the others joined in with some kind of transparent adulation of the official referred to, all keeping wary eyes on Plodder, who at last burst forth,

"You all can think what you like. *My* idea is, he's no gentleman."

Of course Plodder was assailed with instant demands to explain his meaning. Everybody was amazed; but Plodder would only shake his head and mutter that he knew what he was talking about. Nobody could tell *him* what constituted a gentleman. Park wasn't one anyhow, and all hopes for light upon that interview were for the moment dashed; but a day or two more brought everything out in startling colors, when it was announced that Lieutenant Calvin, who had been commanding a detachment "up the country," was ordered to return and explain certain allegations that had been brought to the notice of the regimental commander. Plodder's cautionary signal had been hoisted to some purpose after all.

It seems that being cut off from congenial society, and having no associates with whom to while away the weary hours of his detached service, Lieutenant Calvin had sought solace in the flowing bowl, had become involved in a quarrel with some rather hard

cases among the citizens, and in some mysterious way
the matter had reached headquarters.   Calvin was on
a sort of probation at the time, for his conduct on
some previous occasions had given great cause for
complaint to his colonel, and that officer had now received a note from headquarters on the subject of
Calvin's recent misdemeanor, and felt himself called
upon to investigate.   This note had come three days
before the date of Plodder's last visit to town, and
the colonel had communicated its contents to no one
but his adjutant, and yet it was known throughout
the garrison on the day after Plodder's visit that Mr.
Calvin was to be overhauled, and the colonel decided
to inquire, among other things, *how* it became so
speedily known.

   " I would prefer to have some officer sent from elsewhere to relieve him," he had said to the commanding general in presence of the judge-advocate.   " It
will then create no talk or speculation at the barracks
before he comes."

   " It is known there already," said the judge-advocate.

   " Most extraordinary !" said the colonel.   " I don't
see how that could be and I not know it."   And, indeed, there were very few matters on which he was
not fully informed.

   " It is so, nevertheless," said the staff-officer.   " One
of your—a—subalterns—a gentleman with whom I
have very slight acquaintance, came to me to tell me
about it, as he expressed it, yesterday."

   Then the colonel insisted upon hearing the whole
story, and it came out.   It seems that after one or two

somewhat embarrassed visits, Mr. Plodder had succeeded in finding the judge-advocate alone on the previous afternoon, had then drawn his chair close to that
officer's desk, and, very much to his surprise, had bent
forward, and in confidential tone had remarked, "Say,
I want to tell you about Calvin," and before the astonished judge-advocate could well interrupt him he
had rushed through a few hurried sentences descriptive of the affair in which Calvin was involved, and
looked up in very great astonishment when the judge-
advocate suddenly checked him.

"One moment, Mr. Plodder. I do not understand
the object of this narrative. Have you come to make
an official complaint of Mr. Calvin's conduct? I am
not the person. Your colonel—"

"Oh, no, no. You don't understand, interrupted
Mr. Plodder. "*I* don't want to appear in the matter
at all; but you see I happen to know—"

"You don't mean to say that you have come to me
to give confidential information about an officer of
your regiment?" burst in the judge-advocate with
growing wrath.

"I thought you ought to know," said Plodder, sulk-
ily. "You have charge of the court-martial business,
and I s'pose charges are to be preferred—"

"And you want to appear as a witness, do you? or
do you mean to prefer additional charges, or—what
the devil do you mean?"

"No, *I'm* not a witness," exclaimed Plodder, has-
tily. "I just thought you ought to know about this,
you see, and all you've got to do is to write to so-and-

so, and so-and-so. *They* were there and saw it. Oh,
no, I don't want to appear at all."

"In plain words, then, Mr. Plodder, you came here
as a tale-bearer, and expect me to treat you like a gentleman," said the judge-advocate, rising in wrath and
indignation, while Mr. Plodder sat gazing at him in
pained surprise. "By G—gulp, sir, I did not suppose
the uniform had got so low as that. Go to your colonel,
if you want to tattle, sir; don't come to me. There's
the door, Mr. Plodder; there's the door, sir." And in
utter amaze the gentleman of nigh on to twelve years'
consecutive service slipped out into the hall as rue-
fully ruffled in spirit as though he had been kicked
thither. It was there he encountered Prime and Trickett, and it was in this shape that the interview was
eventually made known to the regiment, but not until
some time after—not until the grand evolution of a
pet and long-projected scheme. Then it was that this
experience of Plodder's was told, with many unflattering comments; and so it happened that not one grain
of sympathy was felt for him in the moment of his
most supreme dejection — the crowning disappointment of his life.

For the first time in his " years of consecutive service " Plodder actually saw a first-lieutenancy within
his grasp, and this is how the matter stood.

Among a lot of desperately, hopelessly healthy
and virtuous captains and first-lieutenants there appeared the unfortunate Mr. Calvin, whose record had
been somewhat mottled in the past, and who was now
in a very precarious state. To get him out of the

way would ordinarily secure for Mr. Plodder only a
step, for at this moment he stood third on the list of
second lieutenants ; but here was a case of unusual
combinations. The senior second lieutenant was at
that moment undergoing trial on charges that must
dismiss him from the service. There was no question
as to his guilt; indeed, he had hardly made any defence against the allegations. But, even were he to
be dismissed, how was that to help Plodder ? Look at
the list:

Second Lieutenants —th Infantry.

1. John B. Riggs (in arrest, undergoing trial).
2. William H. Trainor, *regimental adjutant.*
3. Pariah Plodder.

The army reader sees the scheme at a glance. With
Riggs dismissed, Trainor came to the head of the list,
and was entitled to immediate promotion to first lieutenant, " he being the adjutant." This, then, made
old Plodder senior second, and now—*now*, if he could
only get Calvin out, there were his bars. Under these
circumstances, Plodder was not the man to hesitate.
Knowing Calvin's weakness, he had " kept an eye on
him;" had obtained, through some mysterious correspondent, details of his proceedings at his post of isolation, and it was not long before it began to be suspected that it was he who inspired the rumors that
appeared in the local papers, and so drew the attention of the authorities to Calvin's offence.

Well, Calvin came in, had an interview with his
colonel, who was stern and non-committal. Calvin
protested that his offence had been grievously exag-

gerated. Britton, who took his place up the country, swore that the best citizens up there came in to speak in high terms of Calvin. The men with whom he had had the disturbance were rough characters, who had purposely insulted him, and Britton said that he believed the whole statement could be traced to one of the enlisted men, a bad fellow, whom Calvin had disciplined. The man was known to be writing letters frequently, and no one knew to whom they were sent. Calvin behaved well around garrison, and the colonel was divided in his mind. He hated to prefer charges he could not fully substantiate, and it was by no means certain that the allegations against Calvin could be reliably supported, although there was strong probability of their truth. Then it began to be rumored about the post that the colonel was wavering, despite his firm front against all Calvin's appeals, and that night Plodder was observed to be in a high state of nervous excitement. He had a confidential interview with one subaltern, and sought another with at least one more, but was sternly and angrily rebuffed. "I cannot say what the matter was," explained the offended youngster, "as he made me agree to regard his offer, as he called it, confidential. But it lets me out on Plodder, that's all."

The next day Plodder had a long talk with Calvin. The latter looked infinitely depressed at its close, and went up to town by permission of the colonel to see some legal friends. When night came he did not return, as was understood to be the arrangement, and the adjutant, driving up in the ambulance immediately after retreat, reappeared at tattoo, escorting Calvin; and Calvin, perceptibly intoxicated, was conducted to his quarters, and bidden there to abide in close arrest.

Two days more, and his unconditional resignation was forwarded "approved" from regimental head-quarters, and a few days later, sadly bidding his comrades adieu, Calvin started homewards. "It was no use trying to make a fight," he said. "Some fellow had been spying around up the country, and had prejudiced the colonel, and he told me he meant to bring up charges for the old matter. I could have stood up against them separately, but not collectively; and I had no war record, no friends, no influence. What was the use? Old Plodder gave me a check for four hundred dollars, payable at the First National in Chicago. I'll go back to railroading. Wish to God I'd never left it for soldiering, anyhow!" And with that he was gone, to await at his home the acceptance of his tendered resignation.

Now there was unexpected sympathy for Calvin in the regiment. He was a plain man, of limited education, who had run an engine on one of Tecumseh Sherman's vitally important railways in '64, and when his train was attacked by Hood's horsemen he had fought like a hero, had been made an officer in a regiment doing railway-guard duty, and at the end of the war a lieutenant in the regular infantry. Being sociable, warm-hearted, and weak, he had fallen into drinking ways, had spent his money fast, and so had fallen from grace. He had long been unhappy and out of his element in the service. Perhaps it was best that he should go back to the old life, where drink was an impossibility.

But the wonder was, how could old Plodder bear to spend four hundred dollars of his hoarded gains even for the coveted file? *That* was not answered until long afterwards, and really has no place in the immediate *dénouement* of this plot. It might come in handily elsewhere. He *had* given Calvin four hundred dollars to resign at once, and perhaps the colonel breathed freer at having the case decided for him. Now we were all agog for the result. It depended, of course, upon Riggs's sentence.

Now Riggs was an anomaly. He had few friends in the regiment. He was a shy, sensitive, retiring sort of fellow—a man who read a great deal, was known to be very well informed, a man who rarely appeared at the social gatherings at the store, never played cards or billiards, was civil and courteous to the younger officers, but a little surly to the seniors. He was disliked by most of the latter, and cordially hated by his own captain. When they sat on courts together, Mr. Riggs invariably carried the day in all discussions that came up. He knew more law than any of them. Indeed, there seemed to be no point on which he had not more information than all but two or three of his seniors, and he rather delighted in drawing them out and exposing their ignorance. On the other hand, in the thousand little ways in which superior officers can inflict humiliation upon their juniors, his own and other captains made him feel his dependent position, and poor Riggs, with all his knowledge, was a very un-

happy man. He had not a real friend, certainly not
an intimate, in the regiment; in fact, he incurred the
hostility of many of the subs at the very start by being transferred from an old regiment to near the top
of the list of this one when the consolidation took
place in '71—a transfer that drove Mr. Plodder nearly
frantic at the time, and laid the solid foundation of
his undying hate. Riggs made no attempt to concil-
ate anybody. He never mentioned his past life or services. No one knew his war history, though it was
known that he had served. No one ever heard him
refer to what he had seen or experienced. Yet the
few caustic comments with which he occasionally silenced Plodder's reminiscences amid an explosion of
laughter from the youngsters assured every one that
he knew whereof he spoke. He was sad, dreamy in
temperament; some said he took opium, all knew he
took whiskey, and a great deal of it, though never
was he known to do or say an unseemly thing under
its influence. His face would flush and his speech
sometimes thicken, but for a long time that had been
all. He was what was called a steady drinker, and as
an excuse, his wife (and she was a devoted little woman) was wont to tell the ladies of the regiment who
ventured to allude to it that Mr. Riggs had a pulmo-
nary difficulty, a bad cough, and that his physicians
had prescribed whiskey.

Cough he certainly had, and at times a very con-
sumptive look, and as time wore on he had grown
moody and sullen. Then came an exciting period in
the history of the regiment. Several days and nights

of sharp and stirring service against rioters in the
streets of the adjoining city. Several days with irregular food and nights with irregular sleep, and after
forty-eight hours of such experience Lieutenant Riggs,
suddenly summoned at daybreak by his captain to
command a guard to be sent to some public build-
ings, plunged, stupidly drunk, into plain sight of assembled officers and men, and was sent back to the
garrison in disgrace and close arrest. This was the
offence for which he had just been tried. There was
no hope for him said the colonel and the officers of the
regiment. Dismissal short and sharp was the only
prospect before him. A presidential announcement
had but recently been made that *that* was the one
thing not to be overlooked at an executive mansion
where dismayed diplomats were compelled to struggle
through state dinners unaided by the accustomed Châ-
teau Yquem and Pommery Sec, and rushed away chilled
and alarmed to seek vinous aid for their offended stomachs. Riggs was ruined, and must expect to go.

But the case had been tried before a general court
of considerable rank, and composed of officers from
other posts and commands. Only one of the —th
Foot was on the detail. Admitting the facts alleged
in the specification, Mr. Riggs had called upon one or
two officers, his colonel and the major, for evidence as
to his general character and previous conduct, and they
could say nothing of consequence against him, and *did*
say much that was favorable. When they had retired
Mr. Riggs surprised the court by calling upon one of
its own members, an old surgeon, and subsequently

upon another, a veteran lieutenant-colonel of artillery.

"What in thunder could he have wanted of them?" was the amazed inquiry down at the barracks that evening when it was there announced, and all that was said in reply was, that they had known him during the war. Next day some important documentary evidence was introduced, and then, asking only twenty-four hours in which to write his defence, Mr. Riggs, in a voice that trembled with emotion and with eyes that filled with tears he strove in vain to dash away, proceeded to address the court. "My wife is very ill, gentlemen, and her anxiety on my account has increased the trouble. The order convening the court assigned the barracks as the place of meeting, but it was changed, very properly, to suit the convenience of the members who were in the city. As it is, I have to leave there early in the morning, and be away from her all day. May I ask, as a great favor, that you arrange to meet to-morrow at the old place? I can then be near her in case—in case—" Here he stopped short, and, covering his face with his hands, turned his back upon the court.

The solemn silence was broken by the voice of the old surgeon.

"I know Mrs. Riggs, and have known her for years; she is indeed very much prostrated, and I have a note from Dr. Grant at the barracks substantiating what Mr. Riggs says." The judge-advocate stepped out and had a short consultation with the adjutant-general of the department in his adjoining office, and when the court adjourned it adjourned to meet at noon on the following day down at the barracks.

It was perhaps an hour after adjournment when the judge-advocate of the court, accompanied by one of its members, started out to take a drive. Passing the headquarters building where they had been in session during the morning, they were surprised to see Lieutenant Riggs standing alone at the doorway and gazing anxiously down the street.

"Why, I thought his wife was so sick, and supposed that he would be on his way to barracks by this time," said the member.

"And I, too; I don't understand it," said the junior, who was driving. "At least," he added, hesitatingly, "he may be waiting for the ambulance. It's a six-mile drive, and no hackman will go there for less than a small fortune."

There was silence for a moment as they trotted briskly along. Both the judge-advocate and the member caught each other in the act of glancing back towards the dim and lonely figure of Mr. Riggs, and in another minute the younger officer pulled up his team.

"Major, you want to go back and see what's the matter?"

"Yes, and so do you. Hold up a minute; there's Coles now. He'll know about the ambulance."

Reining in towards the sidewalk, the sauntering quartermaster was hailed, and that somewhat bulky official stepped up to the side of their stylish turn-out.

"Was the ambulance to take Riggs back to the

post? He seems to be waiting for something very anxiously," said the judge-advocate.

The quartermaster started. "Why, yes; I thought it had gone long ago, and had stopped below here where I met it. Captain and Mrs. Breen and one or two others were doing a little shopping, I reckon."

"Meantime poor Riggs is waiting to get back to his sick wife, and has been waiting for an hour," said the legal adviser of the court, with an impatient crack of the whip that startled his spirited grays as they were whirled about and sent spinning up the street, leaving the dazed quartermaster staring after them. At headquarters the team again abruptly pulled up, and its driver called out, in cheery tones,

"Riggs, we are going out to barracks. Can we give you a lift? It may be some time before that ambulance comes along."

"It was to have been here over an hour ago," said the infantryman, slowly. "I don't know what's the matter, and I could not go in search of it; my arrest limits me to this building when in town. I hate to trouble you, yet I ought to have been home by this time.

"Jump in, jump in! We'll get you there in less than no time," exclaimed both occupants. And, only too willing, Mr. Riggs "leaped aboard," and they sped away for the outskirts of the city.

Passing a favorite restaurant, where officers and ladies were wont to rendezvous when in town, they caught sight of the missing ambulance.

"Weren't you ordered to be at headquarters for

Lieutenant Riggs at three o'clock?" demanded the
judge-advocate of the driver.

"Yes, sir," replied that party, glancing in nervous
embarrassment over his shoulder at somebody in the
depths of the vehicle, "but—"

A forage-capped head appeared from behind the
curtain; the benign features of Captain Breen slowly
hove in sight, and a smile of greeting spread there-
over as his eyes met those of the staff-officers.

"Oh, ah! Good-afternoon, colonel. How de do,
Captain Park. Why—yes, there was something said
about going for Riggs when we got through—when
the ladies finished shopping, you know. I was just
reading the evening paper. If you are ready, Riggs,
I—I'll hurry them out now," said the captain, startled into civility to the subaltern on seeing the distinguished company in which he drove.

"Thanks; we won't trouble you. Hup there!" said
Captain Park, dryly and energetically, as once more
the grays dashed off at rapid trot, and in half an hour
Mr. Riggs was landed in front of his quarters in the
garrison.

He said very little as he stepped from the light road-
wagon, but he grasped the extended hands of the two
officers, and looked up in their faces with mute eloquence. The post surgeon happened along at the moment, and Riggs turned eagerly towards him.

"A little easier, if anything," said the doctor, in answer to the look of anxious inquiry. "Better, I think,
than she has been for the last two days. Your telegram cheered her a good deal."

"Excuse me now, will you, gentlemen?" said the lieutenant to his late conductors. "You understand my haste, and will forgive my inhospitality in not asking you in. You—you don't know how I thank you." And with that he was gone.

"Doctor, what seems the matter with Mrs. Riggs?" asked the judge-advocate, impetuously.

"Heart-trouble mainly. Any great anxiety tells right there. She was a very sick woman yesterday. Won't you stop at my quarters?"

"Thanks, no. We were just out for a drive, and must get back."

Whether from motives of delicacy, or possibly from lack of curiosity, very few of the older officers of the —th Foot were present in the court-room when Mr. Riggs read his brief statement or defence on the following day; but nothing could keep Plodder away. Among the group of four or five junior officers his keen little eyes and eager face peered out, ferret-like, glancing from member to member of the court as though he sought to probe their inmost souls. Brief as it was, Riggs had written an admirable little argument. He made no accusations, no recriminations; indeed, he rather slightingly alluded to a portion of the evidence which went to show that during the forty-eight hours preceding his offence he had been kept almost continuously on duty night and day, while the other company officer, his captain, slept almost as continuously. He manfully admitted his guilt, he showed that never before had he been accused of such an offence, and then, with brief refer-

19

ence to the testimony of the surgeon and his old di-
vision commander of war days, and the documentary
evidence in their possession, he threw himself upon
the mercy of the court.

The youngsters could not repress a murmur of admiration as he closed. Plodder with open mouth and
staring eyes looked around the long, littered table like
a military Shylock imploring the fulfilment of his
bond. His eyes brightened as the judge-advocate
slowly rose ; he knew how trenchant he could be, at
least, and he had confidence that his response would
shatter the favorable impression left by Mr. Riggs's
defence. It was with an almost audible gasp of dismay that he heard the next words that broke the silence of the court-room. The judge-advocate calmly
said, " The case is submitted without remark."

Not until Mr. Waterman had plucked him by the
coat-sleeve and hoarsely whispered, "Don't stand there
like a stuck pig, you old idiot. Court's cleared," could
Mr. Plodder be made to understand that all outsiders
were required to withdraw that the court might proceed to its deliberation. Even at the outer door he
again stopped and looked back, a half-formed project
taking root in his bewildered brain, and again Mr.
Waterman unfeelingly interrupted him. " Come on,
Plodder. D—n it all ! are you thinking of going in
and haranguing the court yourself ?" It was in more
than perturbation that Plodder finally sought his quarters and, secure in his solitude, unlocked and uncorked
his demijohn.

In another hour the court had adjourned and gone

its way. Issuing from the stuffy room over the colonel's office, the members had been met by hospitable invitations to take luncheon here, there, and elsewhere about the garrison, and the story of the documentary and war evidence having got around by this time, there was much questioning as to its exact nature, and much wonderment that it had not been heard of before. The surgeon had testified to Mr. Riggs's having been twice severely wounded, once at Shiloh, again at Chickamauga. The artillery colonel to his having twice noticed admirable and gallant conduct in action, which he had praised in orders. The documentary evidence went even further. Evidently Riggs's stock was looking up. Of course no member of the court could give the faintest hint of the action taken, and as they finally drove away, and the officers after evening parade were discussing the probable fate of the accused, the colonel quietly put a stop to speculation by the remark made to the second in command, "He pleaded guilty. They had to sentence him to dismissal. Now only the President can save him. He has no influence, and the President has just said he would not overlook such offences in future. That settles it in my mind."

That night, therefore, Mr. Plodder went to bed half full of comfort and whiskey.

But it was noticed that the judge-advocate, Captain Park, had gone off with the surgeon after the adjournment of court, and while the rest of the garrison were at lunch he, with Dr. Grant, had appeared at Riggs's door.

"She has begged to be allowed to see you," the doctor had explained, "and what she needs is some little word of hope. *His* hopefulness she fears is only simulated for her sake." And nodding appreciatively in response to the doctor's significant glance, Captain Park was shown into the plainly furnished little parlor, where, reclining in a broad sofa-chair, propped upon white pillows, white as her own wan face, was the fragile form of the invalid. He had known her only slightly, but her gentle, unassuming, sweet-tempered ways had often attracted his attention, and her devotion to her husband was a matter that had excited the somewhat envious remarks of Benedicts less favored. She held out her thin white hand, and looked with glistening eyes up into the grave bearded face that bent over her in courteous greeting and kindly interest.

"I wanted to see you and thank you," she said in her gentle voice. "More than once Mr. Riggs has spoken of your consideration and courtesy in all this —this sad affair; but yesterday he was quite overcome. They did not get back with the ambulance until nearly seven, and all that time he would have been kept waiting, and I—"

"It was a pleasure to me to be of any service," he answered; "but I am grieved to see you so prostrated, so ill. Do you know I—I think you are worrying far too much?"

Eagerly she glanced up into his face. "Oh, Captain Park! I know you cannot tell me the sentence; I know you cannot tell me anything they have done,

but I am so torn with doubt, so unhappy ! Mr. Riggs
seems so friendless here. No one knows him, no one
understands him. Last night he almost broke down
as he said that in a whole year yours was the only
voice he had heard that seemed to have a ring of
friendship or sympathy. His people have written to
him to come home. They think he must be dismissed,
and have so written to him and to me. They urge me
to come at once and get the little home they offer in
readiness, so that he can be induced to come right
there if the order is—is against us. I am ill, but if
need be I could go. I would be glad to think of having that little haven for him in case he were crushed
by this, but *ought* I to go? Ought I to leave him
here alone? It will be full three weeks or a month
before we can hear from Washington, I suppose."

Still standing, he bent over her chair. "Shall I tell
you what I think you ought to do, at once?" he asked,
almost smiling. "I believe I will, anyway. It may
be a very rude and impertinent thing to say, but it is
my belief that the best thing you can do is get well—
get well right away, and be ready, you and Mr. Riggs,
to take Christmas dinner with us. Mrs. Park will be
back next week, and I know she will be delighted.
There! It is nearly a month away to be sure, but
that will give you abundant time. Meanwhile, of
course you can't go home. Will you promise me,
Mrs. Riggs?" And the legal adviser held out his
hand, gave her a cordial grasp, and vanished before
she could find one word in which to thank him.
When Mr. Riggs rejoined his wife she was sobbing

like a little child, and yet there was a world of hope
and gladness in her swollen eyes as she gazed up into
his tired face and drew it down to her lips.

As for Captain Park, it was observed of him that
he whistled with considerable cheeriness on his way
back to town, and as he sat at his desk that evening
completing the record of the court. Some weeks afterwards, in speaking of the requirement that no officer
of a court shall make known its sentence except to the
reviewing authority, Captain Park was heard to mutter, " Wonder if inviting a fellow to a Christmas dinner would be revealing the sentence of a court ?" and
somebody present replied, " How could it be ?"

And yet Mrs. Riggs was gaining health and spirits
with every day, and Mr. Riggs, though still confined
to the garrison in arrest, was serenely enjoying life in
her society.

Three weeks later a brace of orders arrived from
the War Department, and there was uproar and excitement among the youngsters in the —th Foot.
Full information of course preceded the official announcement, but the very enlisted men grinned with
delight when those orders were read on parade, for
the story of Plodder's speculation had reached the
ranks, where he was no favorite. Divested of their
official forms the orders were, first, publication of the
proceedings of the court-martial before which Lieutenant Riggs was arraigned and tried, and in accordance with his plea was found guilty and sentenced to
be dismissed the service. All of which was approved ;
but, said the order, " in view of the earnest recom-

mendation signed by the entire court, and concurred in by the commanding generals of the department and of the army, the president has been pleased to remit the sentence, and Lieutenant Riggs will resume his sword and return to duty."

Then came the second order from the A.G.O. :

"PROMOTIONS AND APPOINTMENTS.

* * * * * * * *

"*—th Infantry.*

"Second Lieutenant John B. Riggs to be first lieutenant, *vice* Calvin resigned.   December 3, 187–.

"Second Lieutenant William H. Trainor to be first lieutenant, he being the adjutant.   December 3, 187–."

And Plodder's hoarded four hundred dollars had really purchased Riggs's promotion. "Bless your generous heart, Plod !" burst out that irrepressible scapegrace Trickett as the officers dispersed after dismissal of parade. "Let me shake hands with you, old man. Now just chip in another four hundred and buy me a file and I'll—" But the rest was lost in the explosions of laughter, under cover of which poor Plodder went raging to his quarters.

As for Riggs, he wore his bars for the first time at Park's Christmas dinner, and he wears them yet, only he hates to be spoken of as "Plodder's Promotion."

THE END.

By CAPT. CHARLES KING.

CAMPAIGNING WITH CROOK, AND STORIES OF ARMY LIFE. Post 8vo, Cloth, $1 25.

A WAR-TIME WOOING. Illustrated by R. F. ZOGBAUM. pp. iv., 196. Post 8vo, Cloth, $1 00.

BETWEEN THE LINES. A Story of the War. Illustrated by GILBERT GAUL. pp. iv., 312. Post 8vo, Cloth, $1 25.

In all of Captain King's stories the author holds to lofty ideals of manhood and womanhood, and inculcates the lessons of honor, generosity, courage, and self-control.—*Literary World*, Boston.

The vivacity and charm which signally distinguish Captain King's pen. . . . He occupies a position in American literature entirely his own. . . . His is the literature of honest sentiment, pure and tender.—*N. Y. Press*.

A romance by Captain King is always a pleasure, because he has so complete a mastery of the subjects with which he deals. . . . Captain King has few rivals in his domain. . . . The general tone of Captain King's stories is highly commendable. The heroes are simple, frank, and soldierly; the heroines are dignified and maidenly in the most unconventional situations.—*Epoch*, N. Y.

All Captain King's stories are full of spirit and with the true ring about them.—*Philadelphia Item*.

Captain King's stories of army life are so brilliant and intense, they have such a ring of true experience, and his characters are so lifelike and vivid that the announcement of a new one is always received with pleasure.—*New Haven Palladium*.

Captain King is a delightful story-teller.—*Washington Post*.

In the delineation of war scenes Captain King's style is crisp and vigorous, inspiring in the breast of the reader a thrill of genuine patriotic fervor.—*Boston Commonwealth*.

Captain King is almost without a rival in the field he has chosen. . . . His style is at once vigorous and sentimental in the best sense of that word, so that his novels are pleasing to young men as well as young women.—*Pittsburgh Bulletin*.

It is good to think that there is at least one man who believes that all the spirit of romance and chivalry has not yet died out of the world, and that there are as brave and honest hearts to-day as there were in the days of knights and paladins.—*Philadelphia Record*.

PUBLISHED BY HARPER & BROTHERS, NEW YORK.

☞ *Any of the above works sent by mail, postage prepaid, to any part of the United States, Canada, or Mexico, on receipt of the price.*

BOOTS AND SADDLES;

Or, Life in Dakota with General Custer. By Mrs. Eliz-
ABETH B. Custer. With Portrait of General Custer.
pp. 312. 12mo, Cloth, $1 50.

A book of adventure is interesting reading, especially when it is all true,
as is the case with "Boots and Saddles." * * * She does not obtrude the
fact that sunshine and solace went with her to tent and fort, but it in-
heres in her narrative none the less, and as a consequence "these simple
annals of our daily life," as she calls them, are never dull nor uninterest-
ing.—*Evangelist*, N. Y.

Mrs. Custer's book is in reality a bright and sunny sketch of the life
of her late husband, who fell at the battle of "Little Big Horn." * * *
After the war, when General Custer was sent to the Indian frontier, his
wife was of the party, and she is able to give the minute story of her
husband's varied career, since she was almost always near the scene of
his adventures.—*Brooklyn Union.*

We have no hesitation in saying that no better or more satisfactory life
of General Custer could have been written. Indeed, we may as well
speak the thought that is in us, and say plainly that we know of no bio-
graphical work anywhere which we count better than this. * * * Surely the
record of such experiences as these will be read with that keen interest
which attaches only to strenuous human doings; as surely we are right
in saying that such a story of truth and heroism as that here told will
take a deeper hold upon the popular mind and heart than any work of
fiction can. For the rest, the narrative is as vivacious and as lightly and
trippingly given as that of any novel. It is enriched in every chapter with
illustrative anecdotes and incidents, and here and there a little life story
of pathetic interest is told as an episode.—*N. Y. Commercial Advertiser.*

It is a plain, straightforward story of the author's life on the plains of
Dakota. Every member of a Western garrison will want to read this
book; every person in the East who is interested in Western life will
want to read it, too; and every girl or boy who has a healthy appetite
for adventure will be sure to get it. It is bound to have an army of readers that few authors can expect.—*Philadelphia Press.*

These annals of daily life in the army are simple, yet interesting, and
underneath all is discerned the love of a true woman ready for any sacri-
fice. She touches on themes little canvassed by the civilian, and makes a
volume equally redolent of a loving devotion to an honored husband, and
attractive as a picture of necessary duty by the soldier.—*Commonwealth,*
Boston.

Published by HARPER & BROTHERS, N. Y.

☞ Harper & Brothers *will send the above work by mail, postage prepaid, to any
part of the United States or Canada, on receipt of the price.*

BY W. D. HOWELLS.

THE SHADOW OF A DREAM. A Story. 12mo, Paper, 50 cents ; Cloth, $1 00.

A HAZARD OF NEW FORTUNES. Illustrated. 8vo, Paper, 75 cents; 12mo, Cloth, 2 vols., $2 00.

Never, certainly, has Mr. Howells written more brilliantly, more clearly, more firmly, or more attractively than in this instance.—*N. Y. Tribune.*

This new novel is distinguished by the possession in an unusual degree of all the familiar qualities of Mr. Howells's style. The humor of it, particularly, is abundant and delightful.—*Philadelphia Press.*

MODERN ITALIAN POETS. Essays and Versions. With Portraits. 12mo, Half Cloth, $2 00.

Mr. Howells has in this work enriched American literature by a great deal of delicate, discriminating, candid, and sympathetic criticism. He has enabled the general public to obtain a knowledge of modern Italian poetry which they could have acquired in no other way.—*N. Y. Tribune.*

ANNIE KILBURN. 12mo, Cloth, $1 50.

Mr. Howells has certainly never given us in one novel so many portraits of intrinsic interest. Annie Kilburn herself is a masterpiece of quietly veracious art—the art which depends for its effect on unswerving fidelity to the truth of Nature. . . . It certainly seems to us the very best book that Mr. Howells has written.—*Spectator*, London.

APRIL HOPES. 12mo, Cloth, $1 50.

Mr. Howells never wrote a more bewitching book. It is useless to deny the rarity and worth of the skill that can report so perfectly and with such exquisite humor all the fugacious and manifold emotions of the modern maiden and her lover.—*Philadelphia Press.*

THE MOUSE–TRAP, and Other Farces. 12mo, Cloth, $1 00.

Mr. Howells's gift of lively appreciation of the humors that lie on the surface of conduct and conversation, and his skill in reproducing them in literary form, make him peculiarly successful in his attempts at graceful, delicately humorous dialogue.—*Boston Advertiser.*

PUBLISHED BY HARPER & BROTHERS, NEW YORK.

☞ *Any of the above works sent by mail, postage prepaid, to any part of the United States, Canada, or Mexico, on receipt of the price.*

BY CONSTANCE F. WOOLSON.

JUPITER LIGHTS. A Novel. 16mo, Cloth, $1 25.

EAST ANGELS. A Novel. 16mo, Cloth, $1 25.

ANNE. A Novel. Illustrated. 16mo, Cloth, $1 25.

FOR THE MAJOR. A Novelette. 16mo, Cloth, $1 00.

CASTLE NOWHERE. Lake Country Sketches. 16mo, Cloth, $1 00.

RODMAN THE KEEPER. Southern Sketches. 16mo, Cloth, $1 00.

Delightful touches justify those who see many points of analogy between Miss Woolson and George Eliot.—*N. Y. Times.*

For tenderness and purity of thought, for exquisitely delicate sketching of characters, Miss Woolson is unexcelled among writers of fiction.—*New Orleans Picayune.*

Characterization is Miss Woolson's forte. Her men and women are not mere puppets, but original, breathing, and finely contrasted creations.—*Chicago Tribune.*

Miss Woolson is one of the few novelists of the day who know how to make conversation, how to individualize the speakers, how to exclude rabid realism without falling into literary formality.— *N. Y. Tribune.*

Constance Fenimore Woolson may easily become the novelist laureate.—*Boston Globe.*

Miss Woolson has a graceful fancy, a ready wit, a polished style, and conspicuous dramatic power; while her skill in the development of a story is very remarkable.—*London Life.*

Miss Woolson never once follows the beaten track of the orthodox novelist, but strikes a new and richly loaded vein which, so far, is all her own; and thus we feel, on reading one of her works, a fresh sensation, and we put down the book with a sigh to think our pleasant task of reading it is finished. The author's lines must have fallen to her in very pleasant places; or she has, perhaps, within herself the wealth of womanly love and tenderness she pours so freely into all she writes. Such books as hers do much to elevate the moral tone of the day—a quality sadly wanting in novels of the time.—*Whitehall Review*, London.

PUBLISHED BY HARPER & BROTHERS, NEW YORK.

☞ *Any of the above works sent by mail, postage prepaid, to any part of the United States, Canada, or Mexico, on receipt of the price.*

BY CHARLES DUDLEY WARNER.

A LITTLE JOURNEY IN THE WORLD. A Novel. pp. iv., 396. Post 8vo, Half Leather, $1 50.

STUDIES IN THE SOUTH AND WEST, with Comments on Canada. pp. iv., 484. Post 8vo, Half Leather, $1 75.

A witty, instructive book, as brilliant in its pictures as it is warm in its kindness; and we feel sure that it is with a patriotic impulse that we say that we shall be glad to learn that the number of its readers bears some proportion to its merits and its power for good. —*N. Y. Commercial Advertiser.*

Sketches made from studies of the country and the people upon the ground.... They are the opinions of a man and a scholar without prejudices, and only anxious to state the facts as they were.... When told in the pleasant and instructive way of Mr. Warner the studies are as delightful as they are instructive.—*Chicago Inter-Ocean.*

Perhaps the most accurate and graphic account of these portions of the country that has appeared, taken all in all.... It is a book most charming—a book that no American can fail to enjoy, appreciate, and highly prize.—*Boston Traveller.*

THEIR PILGRIMAGE. Richly Illustrated by C. S. REINHART. pp. viii., 364. Post 8vo, Half Leather, $2 00.

Mr. Warner's pen-pictures of the characters typical of each resort, of the manner of life followed at each, of the humor and absurdities peculiar to Saratoga, or Newport, or Bar Harbor, as the case may be, are as good-natured as they are clever. The satire, when there is any, is of the mildest, and the general tone is that of one glad to look on the brightest side of the cheerful, pleasure-seeking world with which he mingles.—*Christian Union,* N. Y.

Mr. Reinhart's spirited and realistic illustrations are very attractive, and contribute to make an unusually handsome book. We have already commented upon the earlier chapters of the text; and the happy blending of travel and fiction which we looked forward to with confidence did, in fact, distinguish this story among the serials of the year.—*N. Y. Evening Post.*

PUBLISHED BY HARPER & BROTHERS, NEW YORK.

☞ *Any of the above works sent by mail, postage prepaid, to any part of the United States, Canada, or Mexico, on receipt of the price.*

THE CAPTAIN OF THE JANIZARIES.

A Tale of the Times of Scanderbeg and the Fall of Constantinople. By James M. Ludlow, D.D., Litt.D. pp. iv., 404. 16mo, Cloth, $1 50.

The author writes clearly and easily; his descriptions are often of much brilliancy, while the whole setting of the story is of that rich Oriental character which fires the fancy.—*Boston Courier.*

Strong in its central historical character, abounding in incident, rapid and stirring in action, animated and often brilliant in style.—*Christian Union*, N. Y.

Something new and striking interests us in almost every chapter. The peasantry of the Balkans, the training and government of the Janizaries, the interior of Christian and Moslem camps, the horrors of raids and battles, the violence of the Sultan, the tricks of spies, the exploits of heroes, engage Mr. Ludlow's fluent pen.—*N. Y. Tribune.*

Dr. Ludlow's style is a constant reminder of Walter Scott, and the book is to retain a permanent place in literature.—*Observer*, N. Y.

An altogether admirable piece of work—picturesque, truthful, and dramatic.—*Newark Advertiser.*

A most romantic, enjoyable tale. . . . As affording views of inner life in the East as long ago as the middle of the fifteenth century, this tale ought to have a charm for many; but it is full enough of incident, wherever the theatre of its action might be found, to do this.—*Troy Press.*

The author has used his material with skill, weaving the facts of history into a story crowded with stirring incidents and unexpected situations, and a golden thread of love-making, under extreme difficulties, runs through the narrative to a happy issue.—*Examiner*, N. Y.

One of the strongest and most fascinating historical novels of the last quarter of a century.—*Boston Pilot.*

A refreshing and remarkable production. There is here no wearisome soul-searching, and no minute analysis of the trivial, but a straightforward romance, written almost in the great manner of Scott. As a story, it is absorbingly interesting from first page to last. As a resuscitation of history, it has the accuracy without the pedantry of the works of German and other moderns. As a presentation of the physical aspects of the Balkan peninsula, it is very striking, and shows close familiarity with the regions described. As a study of the life and manner of the remote epoch with which it deals, it exhibits, without ostentation, a careful and minute research; and as a literary composition, it has more merits and fewer faults than most of the books written in this age of hurried production.—*Dial*, Chicago.

Published by HARPER & BROTHERS, New York.

Harper & Brothers *will send the above work by mail, postage prepaid, to any part of the United States, Canada, or Mexico, on receipt of the price.*

BY LAFCADIO HEARN.

TWO YEARS IN THE FRENCH WEST INDIES. By LAFCADIO HEARN. pp. 517. Copiously Illustrated. Post 8vo, Cloth, $2 00.

THE CRIME OF SYLVESTRE BONNARD. By ANATOLE FRANCE. The Translation and Introduction by LAFCADIO HEARN. 8vo, Paper, 50 cents.

CHITA: A Memory of Last Island. By LAFCADIO HEARN. pp. vi., 204. Post 8vo, Cloth, Ornamental, $1 00.

To such as are unfamiliar with Mr. Hearn's writings, "Chita" will be a revelation of how near language can approach the realistic power of actual painting. His very words seem to have color—his pages glow—his book is a kaleidoscope.—*N. Y. Mail and Express.*

A powerful story, rich in descriptive passages. . . . The tale is a tragic one, but it shows remarkable imaginative force, and is one that will not soon be forgotten by the reader.—*Saturday Evening Gazette*, Boston.

Lafcadio Hearn's exquisite story. . . . A tale full of poetry and vivid description that nobody will want to miss.—*N. Y. Sun.*

A pathetic little tale, simple but deeply touching, and told with the beauty of phrasing and the deep and subtle sympathy of the poet.—*Chicago Times.*

There is no page—no paragraph even—but holds more of vital quality than would suffice to set up an ordinary volume.—*The Epoch*, N. Y.

. . . A wonderfully sustained effort in imaginative prose, full of the glamour and opulent color of the tropics and yet strong with the salt breath of the sea.—*San Francisco Chronicle.*

Mr. Hearn is a poet, and in "Chita" he has produced a prose poem of much beauty. . . . His style is tropical, full of glow and swift movement and vivid impressions, reflecting strong love and keen sympathetic observation of nature, picturesque and flexible, luxuriant in imagery, and marked by a delicate perception of effective values.—*N. Y. Tribune.*

In the too few pages of this wonderful little book tropical Nature finds a living voice and a speech by which she can make herself known. All the splendor of her skies and the terrors of her seas make to themselves a language. So living a book has scarcely been given to our generation.—*Boston Transcript.*

PUBLISHED BY HARPER & BROTHERS, NEW YORK.

☞ *The above works sent by mail, postage prepaid, to any part of the United States, Canada, or Mexico, on receipt of the price.*

BEN-HUR: A TALE OF THE CHRIST.

By LEW. WALLACE. New Edition. pp. 552. 16mo, Cloth, $1 50.

Anything so startling, new, and distinctive as the leading feature of this romance does not often appear in works of fiction. . . . Some of Mr. Wallace's writing is remarkable for its pathetic eloquence. The scenes described in the New Testament are rewritten with the power and skill of an accomplished master of style.—*N. Y. Times.*

Its real basis is a description of the life of the Jews and Romans at the beginning of the Christian era, and this is both forcible and brilliant. . . . We are carried through a surprising variety of scenes; we witness a sea-fight, a chariot-race, the internal economy of a Roman galley, domestic interiors at Antioch, at Jerusalem, and among the tribes of the desert; palaces, prisons, the haunts of dissipated Roman youth, the houses of pious families of Israel. There is plenty of exciting incident; everything is animated, vivid, and glowing.—*N. Y. Tribune.*

From the opening of the volume to the very close the reader's interest will be kept at the highest pitch, and the novel will be pronounced by all one of the greatest novels of the day.—*Boston Post.*

It is full of poetic beauty, as though born of an Eastern sage, and there is sufficient of Oriental customs, geography, nomenclature, etc., to greatly strengthen the semblance.—*Boston Commonwealth.*

"Ben-Hur" is interesting, and its characterization is fine and strong. Meanwhile it evinces careful study of the period in which the scene is laid, and will help those who read it with reasonable attention to realize the nature and conditions of Hebrew life in Jerusalem and Roman life at Antioch at the time of our Saviour's advent.—*Examiner,* N. Y.

It is really Scripture history of Christ's time clothed gracefully and delicately in the flowing and loose drapery of modern fiction. . . . Few late works of fiction excel it in genuine ability and interest.—*N. Y. Graphic.*

One of the most remarkable and delightful books. It is as real and warm as life itself, and as attractive as the grandest and most heroic chapters of history.—*Indianapolis Journal.*

The book is one of unquestionable power, and will be read with unwonted interest by many readers who are weary of the conventional novel and romance.—*Boston Journal.*

PUBLISHED BY HARPER & BROTHERS, NEW YORK.

☞ *The above work sent by mail, postage prepaid, to any part of the United States or Canada, on receipt of the price.*